Norbury
Park

Other books by Jo (AR) Bradwell

Gasping Thin Air: Mountain adventures by the Birmingham Medical Research Expeditionary Society

Medical books
Serum Free Light Chain Analysis. AR Bradwell (6 editions)
Atlas of Tissue Autoantibodies. RG Hughes, MJ Surmacz, AR Karim and AR Bradwell (3 editions)
Atlas of HEp-2 Patterns. AR Bradwell, RG Hughes and EL Harden (3 editions).

To order please contact:
office@harborneoffice.co.uk

24 Serpentine Road
Harborne
Birmingham
B17 9RE

0121 428 2593

Norbury Park

An estate tackling climate change

Jo Bradwell

Foreword

There are occasions in all our lives when we have the power to do something for the greater good but too few of us recognise them or grasp them when we can. Jo Bradwell has been singularly successful at both recognising and grasping these opportunities. Having spent his career as a doctor and academic, and having created new medical diagnostics which have doubtless saved millions of lives, he has turned his formidable talents to the thorny problem of environmental management.

Nowadays, nobody seriously denies the massive challenges which exist for people and the planet brought about by over-consumption and one of its consequences, climate change resulting from greenhouse gas pollution. Even a cursory excursion into the details of carbon accounting for businesses or governments shows that we have a huge uphill task to curb carbon emissions. Slight modifications to current norms will not produce the magnitude and rate of change needed. Instead, we need transformative thinking about how we need to change the way we live.

In this book, Jo describes the personal journey he and his family have made to both live a better life and to make this count for as many other people as possible. He has merged big-thinking with his natural talent for experimentation and a scientist's instinct for exploration to produce a practical demonstration of how to formulate a nature-based solution to carbon storage. In so doing he has fulfilled his quest to level up his own personal account with the environment while also demonstrating both moral and technical leadership.

Planting trees to solve climate change has become a socially fabricated truism, but Jo set out to test whether this is really feasible. If the problem he had to solve was defined only by the exigencies of nature itself – the weather, soils, choice of tree species, disease occurrence, pests – then his job would have been complex enough. But as he points out, we overlay these natural challenges with a lot of social complexity which just magnifies the overall challenge.

Lots of people hold strong opinions about trees and woodlands in Britain, many deeply based in ideology rather than reality. Having bought Norbury Park Estate in the heart of England with its roots in ancient history, Jo has tried to cut through the social noise by making it work towards a future function rather than some past idyll. He has opened a new chapter on a small piece of England which demonstrates land management practice that could be applied across significant tracts of the English countryside and beyond.

An empirical test of the idea that planting trees can result in carbon storage has been sorely needed. When the subject is stripped of romanticism, such a test can be a template which others can follow. Jo Bradwell was fortunate in that he could afford to take some risks and he has shown that the objective of making land management work as a solution to climate change is hard work and needs determination, design and a dedicated team, but that it is feasible. We learn that traditional ideas brought from production forestry or new ideals brought by people who promote re-wilding have some merits but are generally wide of the mark.

This is a delightful, interesting book which reflects an early stage in a long journey to create a sustainable landscape. Anybody who reads it will be inspired by the vision it expresses, and the systematic, adaptive and disciplined approach taken to pursue that vision. The messages it delivers to the rest of us are that we can all grasp opportunities to transform the way we live.

Professor Sir Ian L Boyd FRS
Former Director General and Chief Scientific Adviser at Defra

Published by Norbury Park Estate, Norbury, Staffordshire ST20 0PP.

This book was produced by Jo Bradwell.

Editor Christine Conlin, 3 Fairbanks Walk, Swynnerton, Stone, Staffordshire ST15 0PP.

Proof reading by Ian Jones, Jinja Publishing Ltd, 39 Newtown Road, Bishop's Stortford, CM23 3SB, UK.

Layout and typesetting by Kate Farrell Visual Communication, The Barn, 36 High Street, Pershore, Worcestershire WR10 1DP.

Printed in Malta on behalf of Latitude Press Limited.

ISBN 978-1-5272-9734-0

To order please contact:

office@harborneoffice.co.uk

24 Serpentine Road
Harborne
Birmingham
B17 9RE

0121 428 2593

Contents

Preface

This is a book about a personal mission to store carbon on a 1,500-acre (600-hectare) English country estate by planting woodlands. Like everyone else, my wife Barbara and I have been responsible for polluting the planet with carbon dioxide, and we want to make amends. We want to put back into the land what we have propelled into the atmosphere over our lifetimes.

On average, each person in the UK is responsible for the generation of over five tonnes of carbon dioxide per year. Another seven tonnes per person is generated in the manufacture of items made abroad and imported, such as cars and washing machines, adding up to 13 tonnes each (Appendix 1). I have produced more than many people since I have flown, driven and consumed more than average. This is partly because of lecturing abroad as a medical academic but also because of travels with the Birmingham Medical Research Expeditionary Society.

Twelve years ago, Barbara and I started our carbon sequestration project. It seemed simple: buy some woods then watch them grow as they absorb tonnes of carbon dioxide – 10 tonnes per hectare every year. If only it were that simple!

After we had bought 130 hectares of woods (sequestering 1,300 tonnes of carbon dioxide per year), it was pointed out to us that, since the trees were already planted, the carbon removal should be credited to the previous owners. The solution was to plant more trees, but this time on arable land – creating woods that no others could claim. So that became our goal: to plant 150 hectares of new woodlands with a potential carbon dioxide uptake of 1,500 tonnes per year – hugely more than our personal emissions of 25 or even 50 tonnes per year.

But it still wasn't easy. It seemed that innumerable people and groups had views on where, when and how our woods should be grown. Planners, planters, commissioners, foresters, rights-of-way advocates, Natural England, Historic England and the Woodland Trust all had strong viewpoints. Then there were the opinions of bat lovers, great crested newt rescuers, deer enthusiasts and bird devotees to consider. Furthermore, having satisfied their demands, we needed full-time foresters, planting machines, tree nurseries and consultants.

Despite all the obstacles, over 11 years we not only planted 406,500 trees but thinned and improved the existing mature woodlands – the total growth potential adding up to around 3,000 tonnes of carbon stored per year. Then we further enhanced our carbon sequestration by planting herbal leys – diverse seed mixtures – on arable land. We reduced our reliance on fossil fuels by installing extensive arrays of solar panels, several wood-chip boilers and fire-log burners and added high-quality insulation to existing buildings. We even subsidized a forestry institute (Birmingham Institute of Forest Research, BIFoR) in an ongoing 15-year project to help understand the future effects of rising carbon dioxide levels on woodlands.

This book is the about our journey: what we have achieved in the first 12 years, how it was done and what more might be possible in the future. We hope that our journey might act as a practical guide and inspiration to others who are experiencing similar anxieties about climate change and are thinking about how they might personally contribute to helping the planet by planting trees and herbal leys.

It has been written for the general reader. Some chapters are necessarily more science-based than others, but we have kept the scientific passages short and accessible, illustrating them with diagrams, photos and graphs. Technical terms are explained in the glossary.

This is not a counter-argument to re-wilding, letting nature take over in its own slow way. Rather, it is about designing the type of woods and forests we might need in the future and identifying how best to manage them. Although some argue that natural tree regrowth is more desirable, it is worth remembering that trees grow faster and in broader species mixtures when they are planned and looked after. Rising carbon dioxide concentrations are the greatest threat to our world, so we need woodlands urgently. Not the scrubland that is the early result of 'natural' re-wilding but big, fast-growing trees – and billions of them. This is what the UK needs to fulfil the promise of being carbon neutral by the year 2050.

Jo and Barbara Bradwell

Dedication
To Barbara and the family

Acknowledgements

My special thanks go to Robin Daniels, general manager and estate director since 2009. He has been involved in every aspect of the estate since purchase as a guiding hand and organiser. He has taken a particular interest in the moated site and refurbishment of the older buildings.

Steve Spencer, the current estate manager of Norbury Park.

John Braithwaite, the previous tenant farmer, is managing the herbal leys and mob grazing.

Phil Argyle of Argyle Woodland Management LLP has been central to the new woodland creation and managing the mature woodlands.

Paul Candlin, Natural England and Staffordshire Borough Council, for planning assistance.

Ruth Keighley, Norbury Park accountant.

Philip Roper of tree consultants Pryor and Rickett, for tree species selection and planting design.

John Winterbourne and Paul Webster of the Forestry Commission for grant support under the EWGS woodland scheme.

The Woodland Trust and Natural England.

Staffordshire County Council and Borough Council.

Keith and Joe Stubbs for building works, Barry Joseph–Lester for architectural works and Andrea Evans at Norbury Parish Council for community liaison in the Parish of Norbury.

Other contributors to the planning, planting, thinning, mapping and measurement of the trees and woodlands include David Shorthouse (previous head forester), Alex Malkin (current head forester), Andy Smith, squirrel control practitioner, plus two postgraduate foresters, Hannah Whyatt and Fraser Wight.

I am most grateful to Amy Cogswell for all her hard work helping prepare the manuscript.

▲ **NORBURY PARK MANAGEMENT TEAM**
Lt to rt: Tricia Turnock, Steve Spencer, Ruth Keighley, John Braithwaite, Shirley Duncan and Robin Daniels.

Introduction

> *"When summer lies upon the world, and in a noon of gold,*
> *Beneath the roof of sleeping leaves the dreams of trees unfold;*
> *When woodland halls are green and cool, and wind is in the West,*
> *Come back to me! Come back to me, and say my land is best!"*
>
> **The Two Towers – JRR Tolkien**
>
> *Reprinted by permission of HarperCollins Publishers Ltd © (1954) (JRR Tolkien)*

The love of trees starts young. Perhaps inspired by a walk in an ancient wood before the age of reason, or a poem absorbed in childhood: "If you go down to the woods today, you're sure of a big surprise…"

Maybe it was the tree in the garden slung with a long swing, a rubber tyre or a hammock, the massive oaks in a neighbourhood park or the towering London planes sheltering in a Royal Park. Or maybe it was on a dream holiday, sparked by an excursion into the jungle or a visit to a tropical forest, home of exotic birds.

Through early adventures or country walks, we all develop a fondness for trees. This is universal; it is built into our genes. Most communities and cultures have revered woodlands or sacred trees. For us in England, the mighty English oak is considered our national tree. The Major Oak in Sherwood Forest hid Robin Hood and an oak at Boscobel in Shropshire hid King Charles II after he lost the Battle of Worcester.

Oak trees are extraordinary. Living over 1,000 years, they are home to more than 2,300 species of invertebrates, birds, mammals and fungi. "Our really old large oak trees support the greatest number of species. We are currently benefiting from trees established hundreds of years ago," says Dr Ruth Mitchell from the James Hutton Institute, Aberdeen. "Out of the species surveyed, 326 were completely dependent on oak and a further 229 highly reliant on the tree."

I was brought up in the countryside, in the gently sloping arable land and tree-studded hedgerows of north Staffordshire, where woodland walks were a frequent childhood outing. Nearby Alton Towers harboured huge Lebanon cedars and flowering rhododendron woods, encouraging my early engagement with nature. My father, travelling around his general practice among farmers and factory workers on the edge of Stoke-on-Trent, would collect injured animals and nurse them back to health. Baby badgers, foxes, hedgehogs and barn owls were carefully fed in rabbit hutches in back sheds. Our two-acre smallholding was home to ducks, geese, hens, pigs and an occasional goat. A greenhouse harboured frogs, toads and grass snakes.

Following in the footsteps of my father, I studied medicine at the University of Birmingham and spent my career in hospital practice. Missing the countryside, for many years I lived on a narrowboat moored on the canal by the University. It was a small tree-covered paradise with a slow flow of water, birds and insects. At that time my primary interest in trees was cutting logs for the small Jøtul stove which kept the boat snug and warm. Cities, rather surprisingly, contain huge numbers of trees, especially Birmingham's leafy suburb of Edgbaston. Tree felling due to road widening, pedestrian security and tree clearing alongside the canals provided me with more than enough wood for burning. Using a small chainsaw and a log splitter, it took me only half an hour a week to chop enough fuel to warm a narrow boat through the coldest of winters.

Before long, I was joined on my boat by Barbara, who became my wife. Realising that babies and narrowboats would not mix, we made the move to dry land. But a house needs more heating and therefore more fire logs. One wood stove was easy to feed but two were impossible. Surreptitiously cutting wood for burning became too demanding. We needed a small woodland instead.

Woodlands grow by around 10 tonnes per hectare per year. Since we kept the house warm with around 10 tonnes per year, a few hectares would be more than enough. After resisting a purchase for many years and coming up to retirement at 65, I finally took the plunge. Having recently sold a University spin-out company, we bought Norbury Park Estate in west Staffordshire. At 600 hectares and with 130 hectares of woodland, it provided an inexhaustible supply of fire logs. But the size of the woods put bigger thoughts into our minds; perhaps there was an opportunity to mitigate our annual carbon dioxide (CO_2) production – maybe even a lifetime of emissions?

Atmospheric CO_2 levels have been rising since 1763 when James Watt started the industrial revolution in Birmingham with his steam engines. With much of the world now industrialised, CO_2 levels continue to rise (Figure 1). Total world production in 2020 was 37 billion tonnes. The UK adds 350 million tonnes per year – 5.3 tonnes per person, 1% of the world total. Since our population is approximately 1% of the total, we are not particularly green.

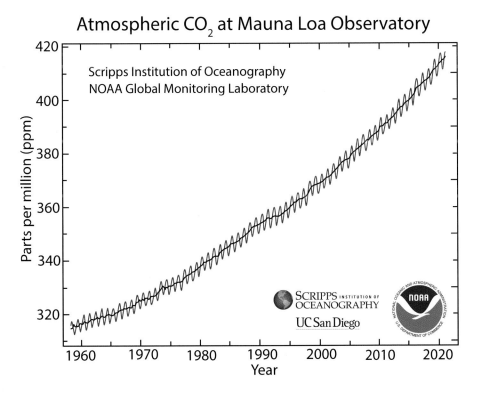

Atmospheric CO$_2$ at Mauna Loa Observatory

Scripps Institution of Oceanography
NOAA Global Monitoring Laboratory

FIGURE 1.
Rising atmospheric CO_2 levels

> ## The UK Government has pledged to be carbon neutral by 2050

Since the UK Government has pledged to be carbon neutral by 2050, our carbon footprint needs to fall – and quickly. Some of our carbon emissions are hard to offset, such as cement production (1.25 tonnes of CO_2 per tonne), so whatever reductions are achieved, some emissions will have to be offset by tree planting. With this in mind, the Government is committed to planting 30,000 hectares of trees per year. At 2,500 trees per hectare for 30 years, this adds up to 2.3 billion trees – enough to cover 3.7% of the UK land area. Since England has 84% of the UK's population (56 million), perhaps it should host 84% of the trees. This would equate to 6.5% of its land area.

We reasoned that every person has to do their bit. Why not plant trees on our newly acquired land – thousands of them to offset our current and even our historical CO_2 production?

This book is the account of what we accomplished. After a brief history of Norbury Park, we describe how we planted, nurtured and managed 310 hectares of woods; how we came to realise that our tree plantations were highly productive in terms of growth and discovered why; how we increased carbon storage in arable land and offset electricity use with solar panels. We even started a timber business to sell our woodland products.

In an attempt to understand the impact of a changing CO_2 environment on mature woods, we sponsored the Birmingham Institute of Forest Research

FIGURE 2.

Norbury Park CO_2 sequestration per hectare in 2020 compared with nine other farms and estates (log scale). (From chapter 8, figure 8)

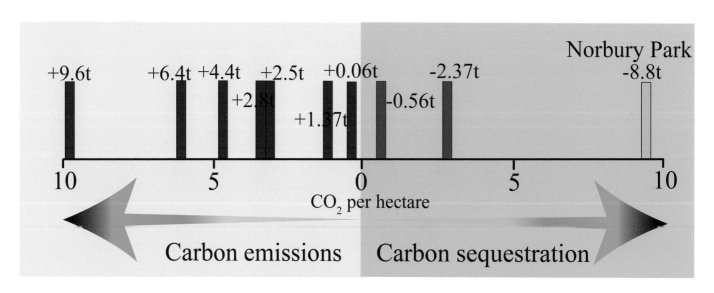

(BIFoR) at the University of Birmingham. Its aims are to assess the response of woodlands to the high CO_2 environment predicted 30 years into the future and to increase understanding of tree diseases. The FACE (Free Air Carbon Dioxide Enrichment) facility started supplementing one of our woodlands with higher concentrations of CO_2 in 2017 (Chapter 7). According to Dr Kris Hart, who manages the experiment, "This piece of Staffordshire countryside may yield extraordinary information that could transform global understanding of climate and environmental change on our trees and wildlife. It is the ecological equivalent of the Large Hadron Collider."

This book is about creating woodlands with a purpose – to offset CO_2 emissions and improve the environment. Guided by science, we have used tree planting to transform over-used arable land, degraded by pesticides and fertilisers, into beautiful new woods. Neglected mature woodland, once only of interest as pheasant shooting cover, is now thriving under active management. It is a wilding that has pulled in the best that science and knowledge can offer.

We demonstrate what can be accomplished on a relatively small country estate in terms of carbon budget, environmental impact and arable-land carbon storage. We might be able to sequester 50,000 tonnes of CO_2 over the next ten years. The results highlight an important role for both large and small country estates to help fulfil our low-carbon future. And what about the UK's biggest land owners, listed in Appendix 2? Could the Ministry of Defence, with its 440,000 hectares, become carbon neutral, or the Church of England, with its 42,000 hectares? And why is there only 0.3% woodland cover in the Peak District National Park (Appendix 3)?

We have shown what is possible and have played our part in reducing the country's carbon footprint. We call on other landowners, large and small, to consider what similar contributions they can make to help avert a global climate catastrophe.

> " The FACE experiment at Norbury is the ecological equivalent of the Large Hadron Collider. "

Chapter 1

Norbury Park Estate – a brief history

Manors, moats and monasteries

Norbury Park Estate covers 600 hectares of land in west Staffordshire adjacent to Norbury Junction on the Shropshire Union Canal. Mentioned in the Domesday Book, it has had few owners in 1,000 years of documented history but there is ample evidence of earlier Celtic, Roman and Anglo-Saxon habitation and only recently, after 230 years, has it lost its royal connection via the Lords of Lichfield.

Map of Norbury Park Estate

FIGURE 1.

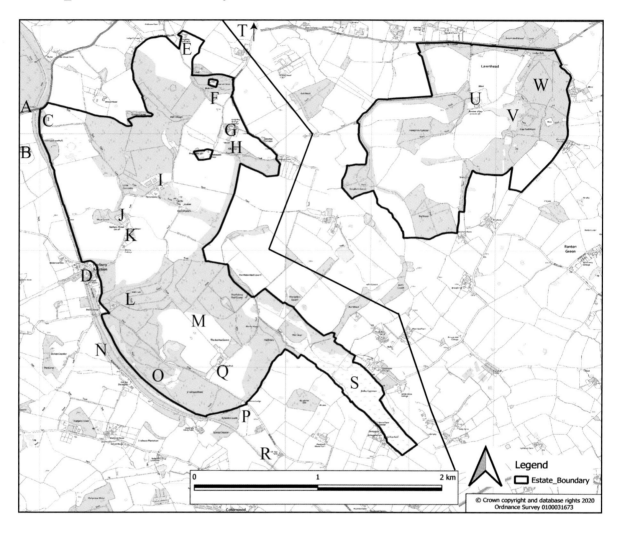

© Crown copyright and database rights 2020
Ordnance Survey 0100031673

A.	Shortest telegraph pole	I.	Campions farm buildings	Q.	Norbury Park Farm and bat barn
B.	Roundabout barrow	J.	Medieval manor and moated site	R.	Final line of Telford's canal
C.	War bunker	K.	Norbury Manor farmhouse	S.	Doley Common. Site of special scientific interest
D.	Granite erratic	L.	Birmingham Institute of Forest Research FACE facility (BIFoR)	T.	Roman camp
E.	*Arborist* practice tree	M.	Original line of Telford's canal.	U.	Ranton Abbey and Tower
F.	Hob Hill	N.	Shelmore embankment	V.	Gap pool/reservoir
G.	Knightley Grange	O.	Shelmore wood	W.	Medieval ridge and furrow
H.	Horse monument	P.	Shelmore lodge		

FIGURE 2. *Triassic sandstone quarry at Norbury.*

Prehistory

Nearby Precambrian volcanoes are the bedrocks on which 220-million-year-old brown Triassic sandstones were laid down when the area was near the equator. There is little evidence now of Norbury's time in the tropics – just brown blocks of sandstone at a medieval moat, stone-work in canal tunnels built by Thomas Telford and some 19th-century quarries (Figure 2). The rest is now hidden by superficial geology moulded by repeated glaciation and alluvial deposits. The result is patchy areas of clay, sand and gravel with a few peat deposits but now dominated by loamy and clay soils.

To mark the new millennium, massive boulders transported from Scotland in the last Ice Age were unearthed and erected in Norbury (Figure 3). Here they stand witness to the parish's location at the southernmost edge of the glacial ice-sheet.

Onto this canvas are painted the signs of four millennia of human occupation.[1]

FIGURE 3.

Five-tonne granite Millennium Stone at Norbury Junction.

Celtic Norbury

As the ice sheets retreated, the trees returned – aspens, alders, oaks, hazel and pine. They were followed by early settlers. A particularly impressive Bronze Age site is an earthwork located on a prominent mound known as the Roundabout (Figure 4).[1]

Bowl barrows, the most numerous type of round barrow, are funerary monuments dating from the Late Neolithic period to the Late Bronze Age (2400–1500 BCE). They were constructed as earthen or rubble mounds covering single or multiple burials. There are more than 10,000 examples nationally across most of lowland Britain; many more have been destroyed.

Despite minor surface disturbance to the centre of the hillock, the Roundabout survives well. It is a rare example in Staffordshire of a bowl barrow surrounded by a ditch and bank, and will contain undisturbed archaeological deposits both within the mound and upon the old land surface at its base.

Nearby stands Hob Hill (156 m), the highest summit for many miles. It looks across Shropshire to the Clee Hills, the Long Mynd and even the Breiddens in Wales. It would have been a commandeering highpoint for ancient Britons and Roman armies.

▲ **FIGURE 4.**   *The Roundabout bowl barrow at Norbury.*

Roman

Evidence of Roman occupation is widespread around Norbury. Their legions would have tramped its tree-covered landscape and soggy soils. The Knightley parish is built on a former Roman military station, known as Mediolanum, while a Roman villa has been unearthed at the nearby hamlet of Forton. Straight roads to the west and south, including Watling Street, testify to Roman domination.

Medieval

Extensive ridge and furrow markings on farmland reveal a past Saxon presence. Norbury village, a settlement owned by Earl Roger of Shrewsbury, was recorded in the Domesday Book of 1086.[2] It included 21 households and was worth two and a half cattle hides in taxation, with land for eight ploughs plus an accompanying woodland one league (three miles) long and half a league broad.

de Knightley family

The prominent de Knightley family originated at the Staffordshire manor of Knightley, at the north edge of the estate, which they acquired shortly after the Norman Conquest of 1066. The Domesday Book lists the tenant as 'Reginald the Sheriff', who held 88 manors throughout England.[2] In 1787, historian Mark Noble wrote of the de Knightley family:[3]

"There is no private family in the kingdom has given more knights; none which has been more numerous in its branches; some of them have almost rivalled the eldest in consequence, and that settled in France surpassed them, having many centuries ago been declared noble; the alliances they have contracted have been equal to themselves, and the many high offices held by them in the state."

FIGURE 5.
Medieval manor at Norbury in 1686.

▼

Sir Ralph le Botiller (Butler)

Butler was a descendent of a Norman knight from the Conquest of 1066. Between 1290 and 1307, he built a manor at Norbury using finely dressed (ashlar) Triassic sandstone, as well as an elaborate moat and fishing pools (Figure 5).

It was sold in 1521 to Sir Thomas Skrymsher. One of his descendents, Sir Charles Skrymsher, shown at the manor entrance,[4] became High Sheriff of Staffordshire. Members of both the le Botiller and Skrymsher families are buried in beautiful alabaster tombs in Norbury Church. The manor and surrounding lands remained in the Skrymsher family for 254 years until brought by George, the first Viscount Anson, in 1776.

Norbury village, was recorded in the Domesday book of 1086. It included 21 households and was worth 2½ cattle hides in taxation, with land for eight ploughs plus an accompanying woodland one league (three miles) long and half a league broad.

18th century to the present: Admiral George Anson and the Lords of Lichfield

Admiral George Anson was a very rich man. Besides inheriting Shugborough Estate in Staffordshire, he had made a fortune fighting the Spanish. After serving as a junior officer during the War of the Spanish Succession, he circumnavigated the globe at the onset of the War of Jenkins' Ear (1739–1748) – again against the Spanish. Starting with five ships, reduced to three after rounding Cape Horn, he sailed up the west coast of the Americas harassing Spanish ships and settlements before crossing the Pacific Ocean. Despite terrible privations, ageing ships and deaths from scurvy, he scouted the seas in search of one of the Manila galleons that traded silver between Mexico and Chinese merchants in the Philippines. On 20 June 1743, in his sole remaining galleon, HMS *Centurion*, he encountered the Spanish ship *Nuestra Señora de Covadonga* off Cape Espiritu Santo. After a dramatic gun fight, it was captured and found to hold 1,313,843 pieces of eight (silver coins from Potosi in Bolivia). He soon sold it for £400,000 (equivalent to £90 million today) in Macau. It was the largest treasure ever captured by the Navy from a Spanish galleon. As captain, Anson would have received three-eighths of the loot – £34 million. Celebrated in England for his bravery and success, he went on to be First Lord of the Admiralty during the Seven Years' War (1756–1763).

Lord Anson died in 1762 without heirs and passed the title to his brother Thomas, who in 1773 also died childless, whereupon his nephew George Adams (from his sister) succeeded to the substantial estates. Using some of the money from the silver bullion, George (who changed his name from Adams to Anson) bought Norbury Park and Ranton Estates in 1775, plus all the lands in between. His eldest son Thomas (the 2nd Viscount Anson), succeeded him and in 1831 was created Earl of Lichfield by William IV.

The Lichfield title subsequently descended to Patrick (1939–2005), the 5th Earl, in 1960 (Figure 6). Known professionally as Patrick Lichfield (rather than Anson), he was a successful society photographer, confidant of the royal family and man about town. Women were an unusually keen interest, demonstrated by 17 calendars he shot for Unipart, featuring scantily clad models in a variety of exotic locations (Figure 7). He also had a string of relationships with noted beauties such as Britt Ekland and Jane Seymour.[5] Famously, he was photographer at the marriage of Prince Charles and Lady Diana Spencer.

Patrick was often on the estate

FIGURE 6.
Patrick Lichfield.

FIGURE 7.
Unipart calendar photograph.

leading shooting parties (reputedly the best in Staffordshire) and photo-shoots. Visitors included Princess Anne with Mark Phillips and Princess Margaret, as well as ex-King Constantine of Greece, Prince Michael of Kent and racing driver Jackie Stewart.

In 1987, Patrick purchased Ranton Estate (see Ranton Abbey overleaf), which his grandfather had sold, and where the main house was a ruin (Chapter 9). His intention was to build a new house that would become the seat for his descendants (Shugborough Hall had been donated to the National Trust in lieu of taxes), but his efforts to secure planning permission only came to fruition a few weeks after he died in 2005.

His son, Thomas Anson (b. 1978), became the 6th Earl of Lichfield but decided not to pursue the building project and was unwilling to look after the 5,300-acre estate. Three years later he persuaded the family trust to sell it for £34.55 million to Graingers PLC, the UK's largest listed residential landlord. It was the first change in ownership for 233 years. The estate was soon broken up into small pieces, many of which were sold to tied or neighbouring farmers.

The shooting estates, containing 130 hectares of woodlands, were of less interest to buyers. For us, however, they were ideal as a carbon offset project. With little forethought, we bought 400 hectares in 2009 (Norbury Park Estate) and a further 200 hectares in 2011 (Ranton Estate).

Norbury Park Farm

FIGURE 8.
Norbury Park House.

▼

During the 1740s, the Skrymsher family (see above) built a house in the Queen Anne style as well as farm buildings on land near Norbury (Figure 8). These were sold to George Anson in 1776. Although not a particularly grand house, its location did lead to a battle in the House of Lords. Growth of the canal system, which required Acts of Parliament to enforce routes through the countryside, brought the great canal engineer Thomas Telford up against Thomas, the 2nd Viscount Anson.

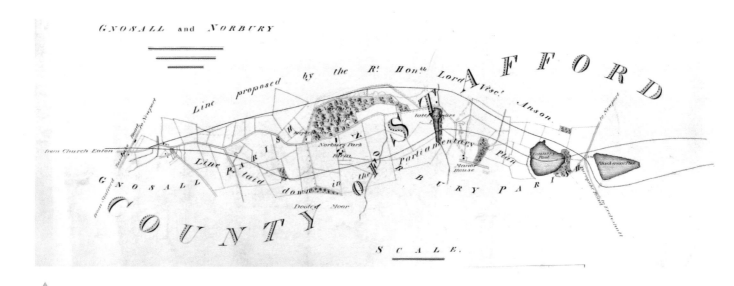

FIGURE 9.

Map of the proposed canal route through Viscount Anson's estate in the 1830s (see permissions p161).

Canals were commercial enterprises so it was financially expedient to build them along the most economical routes. This took the Birmingham and Liverpool Junction Canal (now the Shropshire Union Canal) through the Norbury Estate (Figure 9). Unwilling to have his favourite bird shoot and the outer edge of his lands split in two, Viscount Anson managed to change the Act of Parliament to re-route the canal a few hundred metres to the west. A trivial matter one might have thought, but not so. Instead of cutting through mostly level ground, Telford had to build the mile-long Shelmore Embankment (Figure 10). At up to 20 metres high, it took five years to complete, collapsed several times during construction with loss of life and blocked the through route from Birmingham to Liverpool for two years. Thomas Telford made his last visit to Shelmore Embankment in March 1834, aged 75. Frail and deaf, he was accompanied by his successor, William Cubitt. When Telford died on 2 September 1834, his last canal and masterpiece remained uncompleted.

FIGURE 10.

Shelmore Embankment and Telford's tunnel.

Ranton Abbey

Ranton was the site of a modest Augustinian abbey, founded in 1150 by Robert fitz Noel of Ellenhall. It flourished in the 13th century, before being dissolved by Henry VIII in 1536.[6] Only a tower and part of the south wall, dated to the 15th century, now remain, although the cloisters and other parts are known to have still been standing in 1663 (Figure 11). The buildings were surrounded by a moat; nearby sits a mill with a pond.

After its dissolution, the abbey descended in the Cope family to Sir Jonathan Cope (c.1758–1821), the 4th Baronet. He sold it in 1819 to Thomas William Anson (1795–1854), the second Viscount Anson, who was subsequently created Earl of Lichfield in 1831.

FIGURE 11.
Ranton abbey in 1663 (see permissions p161).

Knightley Grange and Major Robert Hargreaves

▲ **FIGURE 12.**
Knightley Grange in 1960 (see permissions p161).

The escarpment at Knightley has one of the finest views in the area, looking west across to hills in Shropshire and the Welsh border. In 1859, during one of the Anson family's periodic financial difficulties, Major Robert Hargreaves, an industrialist from the Black Country, bought Cob Hall Farm from the estate. On the site he built Knightley Grange, a Jacobean-style Victorian house with 14 bedrooms and a clock tower (Figure 12). Large, rambling and expensive to maintain, it later remained unoccupied for many years. It was eventually sold to Brian Dale, a turkey breeder, in 1967.[6] By now rather dilapidated, the unstable clock tower was demolished, while the house was remodelled and reduced in height. Illness forced Dale to abandon the project, whereupon it was sold back to the Anson family estate in 1995. Having being unloved and unlived in for over 50 years, it was finally demolished in 2019.

History doesn't finish with the written word. Since we bought Norbury Park in 2009, stories of Patrick Lichfield, the estate activities and local characters have abounded. John Braithwaite was farm manager to his Lordship for 30 years and has worked with us since the estate was acquired. Accounts of Patrick's fun-loving character, the Unipart calendar models and the development of the pheasant shoot with Ray Brooks, the head gamekeeper, were fresh on everyone's lips. Tales are recounted of how Gap Pool at Ranton was re-constructed after its drainage during the war and how the big bell of Knightley Grange clock tower tolled hourly over the villages. There is even a story of a Second World War bomber crashing into Ranton Woods, killing all on board. It was a wartime tragedy waiting to happen. Using night-time reflections in Gap Pool as a homing beacon for nearby Seighford Airfield, the bomber failed to clear the trees.

Chapter 2

Woods and carbon storage

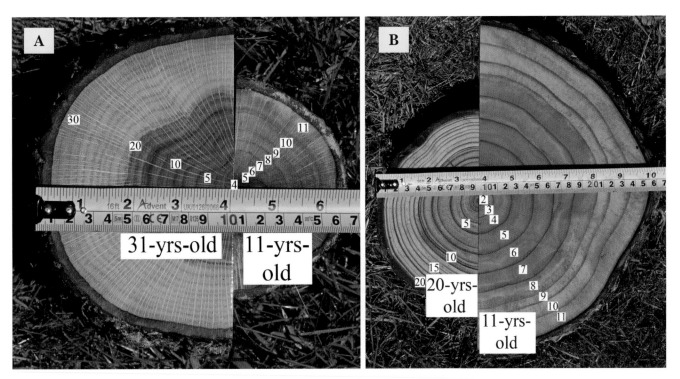

Comparison of A, oak and B, larch grown in monocultures with oak and larch grown in mixtures with halo-pollarding (see Figure 13).

Complex tree mixtures grow faster and resist infections

We are reminded daily about the climate catastrophe about to sweep us away; about governments at home and abroad who are not doing enough to save the planet. And we are told to play our own small part. Perhaps eat less beef, recycle more plastic, turn down the heating and buy electricity from renewable sources. Or perhaps think bigger: install solar panels, air-source heat-pumps and use electric cars – but these are costly items that need government subsidies to gain traction.

> **The carbon in one tonne of tree (about a cubic metre) is equivalent to the carbon in one tonne of CO_2.**

We planned something rather more expansive (and expensive) still. Having sold shares in a university spin-out company, we realised it was possible to offset all our carbon dioxide (CO_2) production by buying a growing woodland. We could become carbon negative as a family and additionally have enough dry wood to feed our log-burning stoves at home.

The computation is simple: the average person in the UK produces 5.3 tonnes of CO_2 per year from a combination of heating their house, electricity consumption and travel. This number is based on the total CO_2 emissions in the UK divided by the total number of people. Although this is an accurate figure, it is unfortunately deceptively low. This is because we import products such as cars, refrigerators and cameras that produce high CO_2 emissions during their manufacture. Adding this 'embedded' CO_2 more than doubles our individual CO_2 emissions to 12 or 14 tonnes per year (Appendix 1). This is the amount we wanted to offset.

The question we needed to answer was: how many trees or how much woodland would we need to absorb 14 tonnes of CO_2 per year?

This is also a simple calculation. One tonne of CO_2 is equivalent to about one tonne of wood. *For the technically minded, the estimate is as follows: carbon (C) has an atomic weight of 12 and oxygen (O) 16, making a combined molecular weight of 44 for CO_2 (C has a value of 12 plus O_2 at 16 x 2 = 44).*

Thus, the weight of carbon in CO_2 is approximately 25% (12/44). Timber in trees is approximately 50% water while the woody tissue is 50% carbon, the remainder being mostly oxygen, hydrogen and nitrogen. Timber is, therefore, also approximately 25% carbon. Hence the carbon in one tonne of tree (about a cubic metre) is equivalent to the carbon in one tonne of CO_2.

FIGURE 1. ▶
Oak wood with bluebells.

The Forestry Commission informs us that a typical hectare of English broadleaved woodland absorbs around 10 tonnes of CO_2 per year. Some trees such as oak grow more slowly than others and obviously trees on mountains are less vigorous than those on fertile lowland soils. Some fast-growing eucalyptus trees might even absorb 25-30 tonnes of CO_2 per ha per year. As a reasonable guide, Barbara and I would need around 3 hectares (7.5 acres) of woodland to offset our emissions.

Having spent a few years looking unsuccessfully for modest sized woodland plots (3-5 ha) in the West Midlands area, in 2009, I chanced upon a website marketing Norbury Park estate in Staffordshire. It had an area of 400 ha and had been part of the Lichfield estate. Most of the land was arable (240 ha) but it included 130 ha of woodlands and a SSSI wetland (Site of Special Scientific Interest) known as Doley Common.

This opened up an intriguing possibility: 130 ha of woodland would sequester around 1,300 tonnes of CO_2 per year – way more than enough for our carbon offset – and there would be plenty of surplus trees to feed our woodstoves. I was hooked.

The estate contained beautiful, 160-year-old, mature oak trees (Figure 1) plus ash, hazel, larch and Douglas fir woodlands. Younger plantations contained 20 to 30-year-old trees plus there were fish ponds, farm buildings and historic houses, all managed by a very capable tenant farmer, John Braithwaite. There were two other attractive features: alongside the western border were two miles of the Shropshire Union Canal with Norbury Junction at the centre while at the estate's northern end was a run-down manor called Knightley Grange (Chapter 1).

The estate was being marketed by Savills on behalf of Graingers PLC. Because it had been on the market for some time as a result of the banking crisis of 2007-8, Graingers

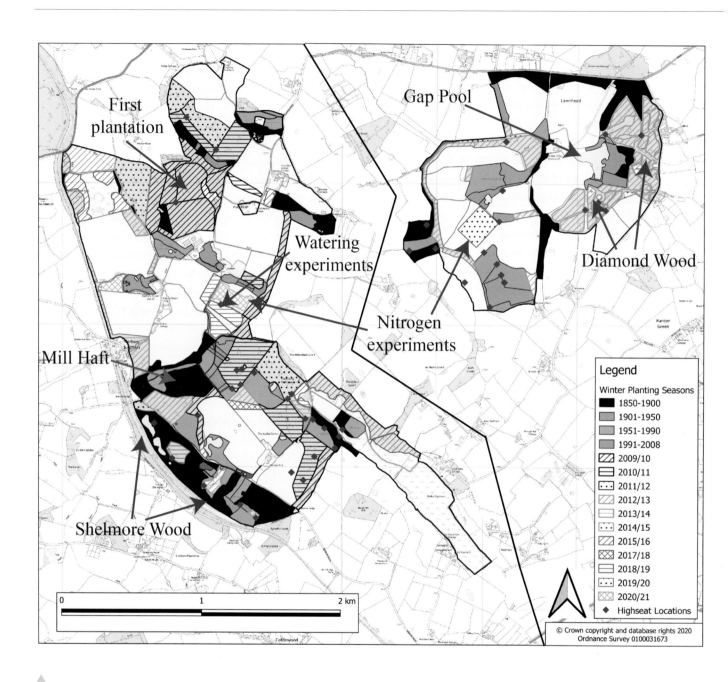

FIGURE 2.

Norbury Park Estate showing 312 ha of mature (160 years), medium aged (20-40 years) and young woodlands (1-11 years). 180 ha has been planted since 2009 with a total of 406,500 young trees on new and restocked sites.

were keen to sell. Within six weeks the deal was done and we became the owners of a complex estate that we knew nothing about managing except for felling a few small trees to sustain our woodstoves.

The woodlands comprised a dozen areas of which Shelmore Wood was the largest at 20 hectares with Mill Haft the next largest at 10 hectares (Figure 2). In total, the woods contained over 2,000 mature oaks planted in the mid-19th century with understories of hazel coppice, ash, witch hazel and sycamore. The younger woodlands aged 20-30 years were also mostly oak with Scots pine nurse trees (planted to compete with and draw up the oak). Smaller areas contained beech, sweet chestnut, larch, Norway spruce and Western Red cedar.

The woods were somewhat neglected because Patrick Lichfield's well-known pheasant shoot came first. Two resident gamekeepers reared 20,000 pheasants and partridges a year for what was described as the 'best shoot in Staffordshire'. The gamekeepers trapped foxes and occasional squirrels but otherwise the woods were 'no-go' areas. Any disturbance to the birds was forbidden so the woods were largely left alone. Although the land manager and army friend of Lord Lichfield, Major Haszard, was an enthusiastic tree person and responsible for planting the young woods, any thinning or replanting of the older woods was resisted.

In the purchase agreement there was an option to cease the shoot which ran from October 1st to February 1st. With the estate under our operation from September 2009, it provided us with six months to understand woodlands before commencing any management changes.

While we were busy expounding to others that we were now 1,300 tonnes carbon negative (give or take a little), it was pointed out that we could hardly claim any credit ourselves since we had planted none of the trees. Any offset had already been factored into the UK's carbon balance by others. The point struck home. We had not increased overall carbon sequestration. Even felling the woodlands and replanting would not increase CO_2 uptake. A true offset would be to plant trees where previously there were none. Over the winter months, we pondered the dilemma. Had we incorrectly boasted about being carbon negative? Could we maintain the illusion or could we correct it by planting new woodlands and then genuinely be able to claim the carbon offset?

We discussed our predicament with the estate woodland consultant. He scoffed at thoughts of planting 100 hectares of trees (to provide 1,000 tonnes of CO_2 sequestration per year) firmly telling me that two hectares per year was the maximum that could be achieved. Having been a little underwhelmed by his inability to recognise a hornbeam tree when tested, I contacted Prior and Rickett, a well-known tree consultancy company. Philip Roper, a director, and Philip Argyle were called in. Their assessment was much more positive. Maybe not 100 hectares in one year, but over five years it would be easily possible. To create 20 hectares of woodland per year including rides (paths between the trees) would mean planting 50,000 young trees a year for five years. We signed on the dotted line. All we needed was to identify the appropriate planting areas on the arable fields and decide the tree species mixtures.

Selecting the best areas was straightforward because the quality of the soil varied; it would be senseless to plant on the best arable fields. The land was predominantly grade 3 (in a range of 1 to 5) but there were waterlogged areas with heavy clay of grade 4 and similarly poor dry sandy patches on higher ground where crops grew badly. Such large variations were due to the estate's location at the terminal glaciation area from the last ice age. Furthermore, the land was not particularly fertile, having been in continuous arable cultivation for over 50 years. With some financial inducements, the tenant farmer John Braithwaite agreed to release the poorer land for trees.

New woodlands with 50,000 trees per year

February 2, 2010 was day one. We made a token planting of a dozen trees the day after the pheasant shooting stopped (Figure 3). During February and March, we planted 50,000 more.

	Common name	Scientific name	Number
1.	Pedunculate oak	*Quercus robur*	5,474
2.	Sessile oak	*Quercus petrea*	5,474
3.	Ash	*Fraxinus excelsior*	8,999
4.	Wildstar cherry	*Prunus avium 'wildstar'*	2,474
5.	Beech	*Fagus sylvatica*	347
6.	Wild service tree	*Sorbus torminalis*	278
7.	Birch (downy)	*Betula pendula*	448
8.	Birch (silver)	*Betula pubescens*	4,169
9.	Whitebeam	*Sorbus aria*	2,981
10.	Walnut (common)	*Juglans regia*	140
11.	Walnut (black)	*Juglans nigra*	140
12.	Large-leaved lime	*Tilia platyphyllos*	3,313
13.	Hornbeam	*Carpinus betulus*	526
14.	Alder	*Alnus glutinosa*	101
15.	Aspen	*Populus tremula*	448
16.	Scots pine	*Pinus sylvestris*	2,338
17.	Douglas fir	*Pseudotsuga menziesii*	2,883
18.	Hybrid larch	*Larix x eurolepis*	1,948
19.	Western Red cedar	*Thuja plicata*	1,754
20.	Yew	*Taxus baccata*	234
21.	Holly	*Ilex aquifolium*	1,337
22.	Bird cherry	*Prunus Padus*	791
23.	Elaeagnus	*Elaeagnus spp*	140
24.	Field maple	*Acer campestre*	791
25.	Hazel	*Corylus avellana*	931
26.	Hawthorn	*Crataegus monogyna*	791
27.	Spindle	*Euonymus Europaeus*	791
		Total	**50,041**

Having little knowledge of which species might be suitable in a warming climate, I suggested a wide variety in order to hedge our bets. The outcome was a typical English native broadleaf mixture together with a few commonly planted non-native species including conifers; 27 different species in total (Table 1).

The trees, purchased from reputable tree nurseries, were bare-rooted and mostly of UK regional provenance, 12-18 months old and with typical heights of 40-60 cm. Crop stubble was treated with glyphosate herbicide and saplings were planted directly into the remnants. They

FIGURE 3.

The first tree. Barbara, Annie (our daughter) and Jo.

TABLE 1.

Tree species in the first 19 hectares of woodland.

FIGURE 4.

Slit plough and slit closure wheels for tree planting with a tractor.

were placed randomly, in rows 2.4 m apart, using a tractor-pulled slit plough with manual insertion into 15 cm deep grooves (Figure 4). Brown shelter guards with biodegradable windows[1] were added immediately and fixed to wooden stakes to protect against rabbit, hare and deer browsing.

Planting density was 2,600 per ha (above the minimum requirement demanded by the Forestry Commission which provided some grant support) in order to provide plenty of choice for later thinning. A small cluster of common and black walnut trees was included, mixed with nitrogen-fixing oleaster (Russian olive) to improve their growth rates (Chapter 3). The trees were planted in random mixtures, whereby no two trees of the same species were placed together. At the time, we had no idea that giving trees a variety of neighbours would prove so beneficial.

Over the following four years, grass and weeds around the trees were controlled by band-spraying with glyphosate weed killer (using three litres/ha) in April and September by means of a tractor-mounted sprayer. Additionally, grass between rows was mown 3-4 times per year for five years. Squirrel control was by drey-poking and shooting in winter plus the use of

live-cage and Kania traps during spring and summer (Chapter 6). The few observed deer were controlled by shooting. When Ash dieback (H. fraxineus) was noted after six years the infected trees were removed annually with the stumps treated with glyphosate to prevent regrowth.

Our first planting season in early 2010 was successful but then disaster struck. April and May of 2010 were warm with little rain. The young saplings burst into leaf then struggled with the drought. 12% died – nearly 6,000 trees. We were horrified. I felt a personal loss. Each death seemed so unnecessary. It was like my patients dying in huge swathes. We had been assured that growing trees was easy – plant and walk away. How wrong we were!

There was nothing we could do. There were far too many saplings to water and it would be cheaper to replant in the autumn. I nursed my emotional wounds over the summer, consulting on where we had gone wrong but intent on planting more, but perhaps in a more drought-

resistant mixture.

During the winter of 2010/2011 we planted additional areas with 50,000 trees plus the 'beat up' of 6,000 (a term referring to replacing young dead trees), restocking like-for-like. We did this by hand but the outcome was poor since May 2011 was again very dry with a similar death rate. One area of 5,000 trees was so badly affected that we replaced them all so we could re-plant with tractor and plough. Planting so many trees which then died was heart-breaking. We even tried spraying one plot with water from our reservoir but it was too little, too late and impossible to water them all. I now realise why farmers always worry about the weather.

I was reassured repeatedly that it was just bad luck and that April, May and June were normally much wetter. Indeed, this was to prove the case. The winter planting of 2012 was followed by wet spring weather with 98% tree survival. Fortunately, this was when we planted our next woodland.

FIGURE 5.

Winning photograph by Ali Cameron (aged 14) of the Ranton Diamond Wood on the community planting day. Children from a dozen schools also helped.

Ranton Diamond Wood

To celebrate the Queen's Diamond Jubilee (60 years), the Woodland Trust organised a tree planting project based on 60 named **Diamond Woods** nationwide of 60 acres (25 ha) each.

We applied for the honour and were allowed to name our 2012 planting Ranton Diamond Wood. The following account, including a competition-winning photograph, can be found in the Royal Record 2012, published by the Woodland Trust (Figure 5).[1]

"Set within the grounds of Norbury Park Estate in Staffordshire, Ranton Diamond Wood has been planted across 28 hectares of land, adjacent to the landscaped park of mature oaks, an arboretum and a reservoir. This Diamond Wood is a fine setting for some 50,200 native trees that were planted with help from the local community.

Although the wood is dominated by oak, largely grown from the acorns of other trees on the estate, around 30 different tree species have been planted in distinct compartments. When mature, individual tree species will dominate their own area imparting different characteristics to each part of the wood.

Ranton Diamond Wood also boasts six Royal oaks, which have been planted in specially chosen locations, including an island in the centre of a pond and in the heart of a yew hedge maze. Visitors to the estate will be encouraged to undertake a 'Royal Oak Trail' to discover all six of these magnificent trees on a route that takes them to all parts of the woods.

Norbury Park Estate is the perfect location to commemorate the Jubilee due to its existing royal heritage. Not only was it a favourite spot of the Queen's cousin, Lord Lichfield, but it is also only a few miles from the famous Royal oak that sheltered Charles II after the battle of Worcester. Now, this Diamond Wood takes its own place in history."

More years of tree planting

Over six years, we planted 140 ha with over 300,000 trees to complete the main afforestation project (Figure 2). We included tree corridors connecting separate woods to safeguard the movement of animals and birds. There remained a few small areas with relatively poor arable land which we later covered with further plantations. Some included exotic species including eucalyptus, redwoods (Figure 7), catalpas, magnolias plus numerous

FIGURE 7.
*Coast redwoods in
a conifer plantation.*

Key			
1	Mixed native	23	Whitebeam
2	Community area	24	Hazel
3	Wild cherry	25	Mixed native
4	Scots pine	26	Crab apple
5	Beech	27	Mixed native
6	Sweet chestnut	28	Rowan
7	Yew	29	Lime
8	Mixed native	30	Mixed native
9	Mixed native	31	Mixed native
10	Mixed native	32	Wych elm
11	Field maple	33	Mixed native
12	Privet	34	Mixed native
13	Holly	35	White/crack willow
14	Juniper	36	Mixed native
15	Bird cherry	37	Mixed native
16	Mixed native	38	Bay willow
17	Blackthorn	39	Mixed native
18	Mixed native	40	Wild service
19	Black poplar	41	Hornbeam
20	Mixed native	42	Lime
21	Mixed native	43	Mixed native
22	Dogwood		
★	Royal Oak		

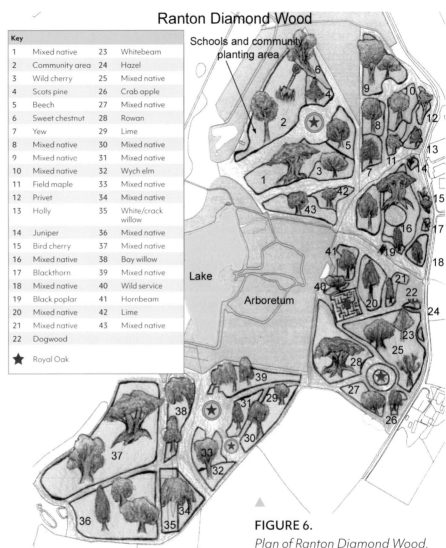

FIGURE 6.
Plan of Ranton Diamond Wood.

others – over 100 different types in total (Appendix 4) while another contained a conifer mixture (Appendix 5).

Alongside the main planting schemes, we thinned the older woodlands. Because of their relative neglect, many trees had become suppressed, too crowded or were in poor condition. There were several acres of pure ash plantations that had ash die-back and numerous trees with acute oak decline which were removed. Also, there were grey squirrel infestations (Chapter 6) that had caused severe damage in some younger woods – these trees were also felled.

As the timber milling operation expanded (Chapter 4), we progressively removed poorer trees and replanted the areas with mixtures of native and foreign species that usually included oak as a final crop. One remote area in Shelmore wood contained a small stream filled with silt that had not been dredged for 100 years. Attempts to drain it before planting trees nearly ended with us almost losing a digger in the mud (Figure 8).

FIGURE 8.
Digger sinking in mud.

FIGURE 9.

Tree racks were created in year seven by removing every 7th row of trees.

Managing the complex woodlands

We then faced recurring enquiries about how we were we going to manage our complex woods. Traditional forestry in single-species woodlands involves repeatedly thinning then clear-felling at maturity. In contrast, we wished to preserve our complex mixtures since we were not sure which species might thrive in a changing climate.

It was only after the trees were planted that we discovered from publications in the scientific literature that complex mixtures usually sequester more carbon (Chapter 3).[2] It was apparent that forest growth and resilience are enhanced if plantings include trees with differing features such as leaf shapes and sizes, height, soil requirements and disease resistance.

As the canopy closed around year seven, we removed every 7th row of trees (Figure 9) to allow easy access to the winners ie. those with the most vigorous growth and best form. Typically, we identified around 250 trees per hectare out of the 2,600 per hectare that we planted. For timber production we wanted a final crop of not just oak, but other species that grew vigorously, such as Western Red cedar and larch. Importantly, specimens of every species, including conifers, were conserved. In the process, we extracted 100 tonnes of small logs that were processed into fire-logs and wood chip.

Enhanced growth rates noted in the mixed species woodlands

Much to our surprise, when we came to measuring the size of the trees, we found that they were growing faster than we could have dared hope. It seemed that our complex woodlands, planted on rather modest soils, were in robust health.[3] This was despite low rainfall during May in the first two years that caused nearly 20% mortality. Also, it was apparent that Douglas fir growth in the mixed plantations was higher than those planted at the same time in an adjacent pure plantation of Douglas fir that were infected with woolly aphids.

As we became convinced that complex mixtures promote high growth rates, we decided not to remove trees in the thinning process. Instead, we pollarded trees around our selected winners. The process involves cutting them at 6-8 feet above ground, and above the bottom ring of branches so that none die (Figure 10). We call this halo-pollarding as opposed to halo-thinning in which trees around

FIGURE 10.

Pollards around a Scots pine.

selected winners are removed completely.[4] The latter is a technique of active silviculture (cultivation of trees) used in France to promote the growth of winners. By removing shade-bearing trees, the winners are exposed to full sunlight that allows faster growth (termed free growth).

For us, halo-pollarding has several advantages.

1. The complex mixture of trees is maintained with accompanying fast growth and reduced infection rates.
2. Regrowth of shoots from pollarded trees shields the trunks of the winners from sunlight thereby suppressing epicormic (new) growth on their stems.
3. Since all trees are retained, the surviving intertwined roots enhance wind stability and maintain complex root interactions.
4. Since roots comprise 25% of woodland biomass, retaining all the trees enhances carbon sequestration underground.

In addition, we high-prune the winners to one third of their height to enhance timber quality.

Within two years, the canopy had closed again necessitating a further round of stem pruning and halo-pollarding. In the four subsequent years of this active management, the high growth rates are being maintained and the woods are healthy. Eight species are shown in Table 2 alongside yield classes from Forestry Commission tables.[5] It is clear that most trees are as big as or larger than those in reference tables.

TABLE 2.
Average size of 11-year-old trees in the mixed plantation compared with the Forestry Commission *yield class (YC) ranges.*

Species	Diameter at breast height	Top height	Yield class	FC *yield class range*
Douglas fir (pure)	12 cm	7.3 m	20	8-24
Douglas fir (mixed)	14 cm	8.7 m	24	8-24
Hybrid larch	24 cm	11.9 m	20	4-14
Lime	11 cm	6.4 m	6	4-12
Oak (*robur*)	9 cm	6.0 m	8	4-8
Scots pine	14 cm	7.0 m	16	4-14
Silver birch	16 cm	11 m	14	4-12
Western Red cedar	15 cm	7.3 m	28	12-24
Wildstar cherry	13 cm	8.5 m	12	4-8

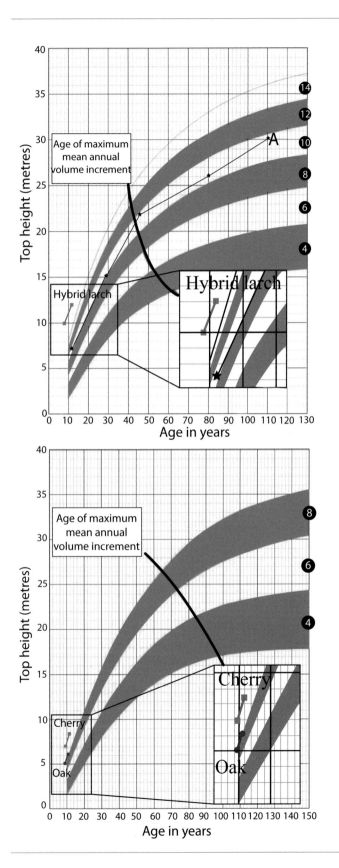

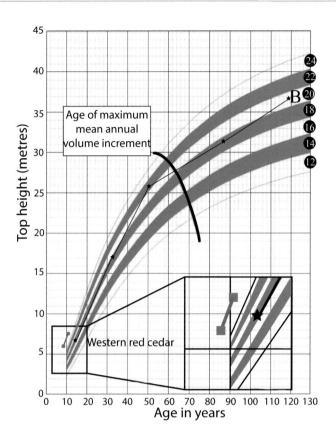

Figure 11 shows growth rates for four of these tree species plotted on Forestry Commission yield class curves. This data shows that our 11-year-old plantations have the size of some 20 to 25-year-old woodlands elsewhere.

Size measurements on some of the faster growing trees are shown in Figures 12A and 12B. Table 3 and Figure 13 compare the annual rings with trees from elsewhere on the estate. These are the growth rates one might normally expect from many trees grown in monocultures.

FIGURE 11.

Forestry Commission growth curves for hybrid larch, Western Red cedar, cherry and oak. Lines A and B represent typical growth curves. Tree sizes in Norbury woods for each species at years 9 and 11 are shown in the inserts. Numbers on the right axis refer to tonnes of wood per ha per year for different growth rates during the life cycle of the trees.

FIGURE 12A.

Figure 12A. Diameters at breast height at 11 years for: A, oak (12 cm) B, cherry (22cm) and C, larch (34 cm) in mixed woodlands (from Table 3).

 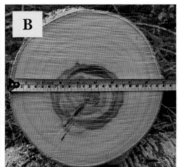 

FIGURE 12B.

Tree ring growth (breast height) at 11 years (Figure 12A) for A, oak (12 cm) B, cherry (22cm) and C, larch (34 cm) (from Table 3).

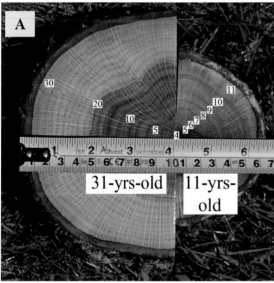 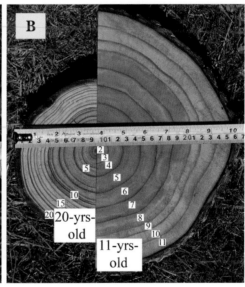

FIGURE 13.

Comparison of A, oak and B, larch grown in monocultures with oak and larch grown in mixtures with halo-pollarding (from Table 3).

	Oak A	Oak P	Cherry A	Cherry P	Larch A	Larch P
Age	11 years	31 years	11 years	29 years	11 years	20 years
DBH	12 cm	20 cm	22 cm	19 cm	34 cm	20 cm
Height	6.8 m	12.2 m	11.2 m	5.8 m	13.2 m	16.5 m

TABLE 3

Comparison of tree growth with active silviculture (A) in the mixed woodlands compared with passive silviculture (P) in monocultures (see Figure 13).

It is likely that there are several reasons for the high tree growth rates but halo-pollarding and reduced infection rates would have been important (Chapter 3). Good squirrel and deer control would also have helped (Chapter 6).

Since our first objective is to store carbon (Chapter 8) and our second to produce high-quality timber (Chapter 4), we will continue to focus on nurturing the most vigorous, straight young trees. Over the next few years, we will confirm the final winners and oversee their growth to maturity while continuing to maintain species diversity. While it is impossible to predict the future with such huge changes occurring in the climate and the rapid spread of tree infections, we imagine that the trees should follow the growth curves shown in Figure 11. Oak trees might be able to increase their girth by one cm per year for 100 years as recently described for a 93 cm diameter tree (dbh) in 91 years in Micheldever Wood, Hampshire.[6]

The amount of carbon sequestered at Norbury Park is discussed later (Chapter 8). However, in 2020, the woodlands contributed 2,959 tonnes in 2020 (Figure 14).

The extra cost of our intensive early silviculture is about £1,000 per hectare (in 2020). We anticipate that this will translate into faster crop rotations. As a fully stocked hectare of mature prime oak woodland might be worth £70,000 (£1,000 per tree)[7] increasing the growth rate by a few years makes good financial sense.

The other benefit is the reduction in land required for the same amount of carbon storage. Arable land costs over £20,000 per hectare so if growth rates continue to be more than 50% above normal, it would massively reduce the amount of land required to plant billions of trees as the UK government has promised.

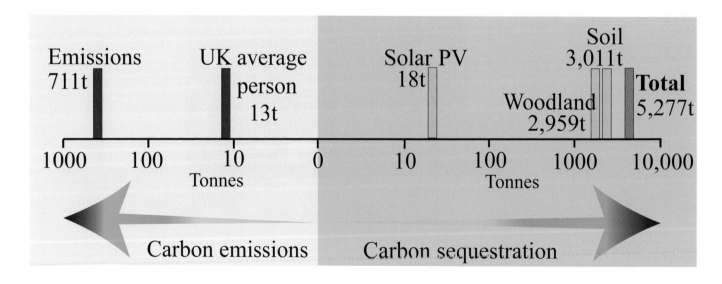

FIGURE 14.

Contribution of the woodlands to overall CO_2 sequestration at Norbury Park in 2020.

Complex mixtures should include trees from other countries

A question that is always asked is: which tree species to plant in complex woodlands? Our answer is that while maintenance of natural habitats is important, native British species are limited in number as relatively few have been able to colonise the country since the last ice age (Chapter 3). Wider selections that include species from other temperate climatic regions can only improve forest robustness in a changing climate (Figure 15). Species chosen should preferably have different physical characteristics and perhaps be widely separated genetically. It should be noted that widening species selections for new woodlands beyond native broadleaves is recommended in numerous articles in the Quarterly Journal of Forestry.[8-10]

▼ **FIGURE 15.**
Tulip tree (from the USA).

▲
Eucalyptus trees.

Harvesting

I am also frequently asked: how do we intend to harvest our complex mixtures and at what cost? My reply is that despite there being hundreds of different species in the Amazon and Congo forests, loggers seem to have no problems removing valuable individual trees while maintaining their neighbours. There is no reason why foresters in the UK should not be equally as adept.

How fast can tree mixtures grow when watered and fed?

Our tree mixtures are growing quickly. Needless to say, they might grow even faster if they were watered during dry spells and fed an optimal mixture of nutrients. After all, this policy is often used to promote fruit tree growth. Since we have a large reservoir at Norbury that was frequently used to water potato fields, we decided to try watering and feeding a young woodland to see how it might respond. We aim to keep the soil moisture content at between 30-40% on a continuous basis and to add nutrients as needed.

Using this regimen, we planted a hectare of 10 different species that included 50% oak trees (Q. robur) from Holland, France and England together with silver birch and common alder. In addition, we planted another hectare of 10 species from northwest USA that included Coast redwoods, Douglas fir and Grand fir (Appendix 6). To compare growth rates with untreated trees, we added small control plantations that are identical but not watered or fed.

As expected, even though the trees are very young they are growing quickly. Figure 16 shows an oak tree after six months' growth from its start at 40 cm. It has put on well over a metre in height. Other trees have shown similar huge growth rates compared with the control plots. Only time will tell as to whether these growth rates are maintained and whether there are any adverse effects on timber quality (Chapter 3).

FIGURE 16.

Two year old oak tree – watered and fed.

Nitrogen-fixing experiment

High CO_2 levels augment plant and tree growth. For example, this is widely used in horticulture for enhancing the growth of tomatoes. Experiments on increasing CO_2 in forestry show the same effect (Chapter 7). At first sight, this is good news as more CO_2 will be absorbed from the atmosphere. Furthermore, in a higher CO_2 environment, trees need less water – yet more good news since droughts are predicted to be more prevalent in the future.

The next critical requirement for tree growth is nitrogen – an essential component of all proteins found in living tissues. Since many forest soils are nitrogen depleted, its shortage is likely to limit enhanced tree growth rates. This is the same with arable crops. Adding nitrogen fertiliser is a mainstay of agriculture across the world. Recent evidence from the BIFoR FACE experiment (Chapter 7) indicates that nitrogen is being depleted from the soil as the trees accelerate their growth under higher CO_2 concentrations.

Fortunately, many plant species have a symbiotic relationship with bacteria on their roots that chemically trap nitrogen from the air and convert it into available nitrates. The plants feed the bacteria with sugars from photosynthesis while the bacteria feed the plants with nitrates for protein production. Clover is a fine example and by planting it into grass mixtures it allows them to grow well without the need for additional nitrogen fertilisers (Chapter 5).

Similarly for trees. Around the world there are over 650 tree species that have nodules on their roots containing nitrogen-fixing bacteria. Most are found in the tropics and the only native species that fixes nitrogen is common alder. However, many other nitrogen-fixing species grow well in Britain such as red alder, false acacia, laburnums and oleasters. There have been several studies showing that planting such nitrogen-fixing trees in a woodland mixture enhances growth rates (Chapter 3). However, they are not widely used or recommended, perhaps because of a lack of guidelines or clear scientific evidence.

If the availability of nitrogen is a limiting factor in a higher CO_2 environment, planting nitrogen-fixing trees would be very beneficial. With this in mind, we have commenced experiments on two four-hectare

> " Studies have shown that planting nitrogen-fixing trees in woodlands enhances growth rates. "

sites (Figure 2). Mixtures of 36 different trees that include five nitrogen-fixing species in varying amounts have been planted in complex mixtures (Figures 17 and 18 and Appendix 7). This might allow us to estimate the percentage of nitrogenating trees required in a complex mixture to promote maximum tree growth (Whyatt et al).[11]

▲ FIGURE 17.
Young trees in a nitrogen-fixing experiment.

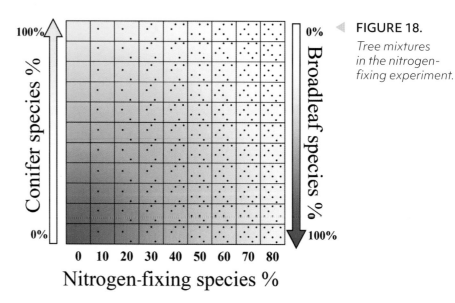

◀ FIGURE 18.
Tree mixtures in the nitrogen-fixing experiment.

Conclusion

Twelve years down the line, we believe that our woodland planting and management practices at Norbury Park offer an encouraging and practicable model for landowners and planners of new woodlands to adopt elsewhere in the UK. The trees we have planted in complex mixtures have suffered few infections and their increased growth rates bode well for their greater CO_2 storage capacity over their lifetimes. Such plantations would also considerably reduce the land area currently considered necessary to achieve the same amount of carbon storage.

As we have come to realise, forest growth and resilience are enhanced if plantations consist of trees with differing features such as leaf shapes and sizes, height, soil requirements and disease resistance. Between neighbours of different species, there is less competition for nutrients, water and sunlight and creating distance between individuals of the same species also means disease transmission is reduced. But as there are relatively few British tree species and as many of these are subject to damaging infections, it is advisable to add non-native trees to planting mixes to ensure forest robustness during rapid climate change.

It might also be opportune to include nitrogen-fixing species to help support the rapid tree growth rates which are predicted to result from increasing CO_2 concentrations in the atmosphere.

In 2018, our complex woodlands and innovative management techniques were recognised by being presented with The Sylva Trophy from the Royal Forestry Society and The Peter Saville Award from Woodland Heritage (Appendix 9).

THE WOODLAND TEAM.
The woodland team. Lt to rt: Lee Beardmore, Andy Smith, Kevin Ward, Hannah Whyatt, Matthew Bennion, Pete Malpas, Alex Malkin, David Goodfellow (kneeling).

Chapter 3

How woodland tree mixtures increase carbon uptake

◁ New plantation.

Eight years later. ▷

▲ Woolly aphids on Douglas fir trees in (A) a monoculture of Douglas fir and (B) in a neighbouring mixed species plantation (see page 47).

Mixed plantations store more carbon and are more resilient to climate change

Traditional forestry in the UK has been based on monocultures, mostly conifers.

1. Mixed plantations store more carbon

Vast areas of England, Scotland and Wales have been covered in impenetrable, dark and dreary columns of Sitka and Norway spruce, larch and Scots pine. They may be fast growing, commercially valuable and easy to harvest, but they are prone to disastrous insect and fungal infections which can reduce plantations to ecological wastelands. Examples include the billions of lodgepole pine trees killed in North America by beetles (Figure 1) and similar decimation of spruce forests in the Harz Mountains of Germany. Thankfully, the policy of conifer monocultures is now changing. New woodlands are being planted with many different species and with them come all the benefits of increased growth rates,

▲ **FIGURE 1.**   *Dead forests in Canada from pine beetle infections.*

ecological resilience and beauty.

The purpose of this chapter is firstly to consider the evidence that tree mixtures grow faster than monocultures and secondly to explore some of the intricate mechanisms responsible for increased growth rates.

a. Increased growth rates in mixed species natural woodlands

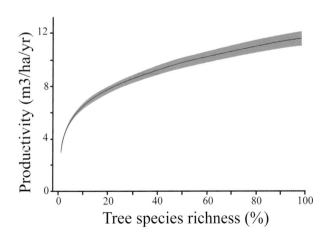

Many publications in the scientific literature show that complex tree mixtures grow faster than monocultures – referred to as 'over-yielding'. A recent study of more than 750,000 sample plots in global natural forests showed that higher species diversity was associated with up to fourfold more carbon uptake than monocultures.[1] This correlation is known as the 'biodiversity-productivity

◁ **FIGURE 2.**

Productivity increases with more complex mixtures. The red area shows one standard deviation (¹ see permissions p161).

relationship', with productivity being the volume of woody mass produced in a forest per year (Figure 2). Each 10% loss of diversity corresponds to a 6-7% decline in productivity. Such colossal data sets provide overwhelming evidence that in natural forests, species complexity is important for growth rates.

Some natural forests are remarkably diverse. For example, a one-hectare plot in Bahia, Brazil, contained 405 different tree species.[1] By contrast, the whole of Britain has just 32 native species.

b. Over-yielding in planted woodlands

A similar biodiversity-productivity relationship is observed when multiple tree species are planted experimentally. For example, when a subtropical forest in China was established with 150,000 trees in plots of 1 to 24 different species, it was apparent that greater mixture richness was strongly associated with increased growth rates. The most complex combinations accumulated nearly twice the amount of carbon as monocultures (Figure 3).[2] Furthermore, increased productivity was at its highest when tree species had greater differences in shape and function and were not genetically related.

An experiment in a young, temperate woodland in the USA showed similar results: more complex mixtures grew faster. This depended partly on species neighbours but the fastest growth for red maple, for example, was seen in the maximum mixture of 12 species (Figure 4).[3]

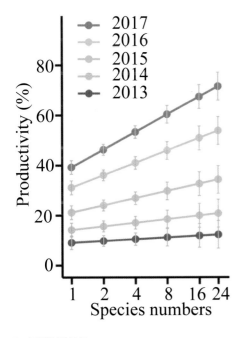

FIGURE 3.

High species complexity correlates with more carbon storage ([2] see permissions p161).

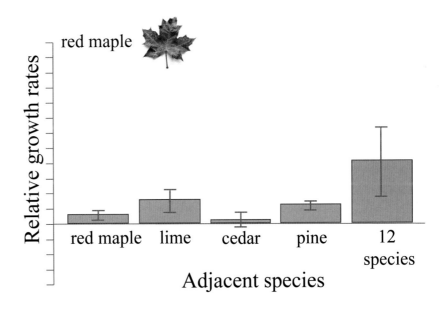

FIGURE 4.

Maple tree growth rates depended upon their neighbours and the total mixture.

c. The Darwin effect

In his famous book *On The Origin of Species* published in 1859, Charles Darwin noted what happened when different grasses were grown together (see Chapter 5).[4] One might presume that the average yield for a given area planted with three different species would simply be the average of the expected yields for each species. In fact, it is higher than this, an over-yielding phenomenon that is sometimes called the Darwin effect (Figure 5). A 50% increase in the total growth mass of the mixture was attributed to the different species varying in factors such as root depth, leaf and branch growth, growth periods, sensitivity to pathogens and infection rates, meaning that mixtures are better able to utilise all available resources.

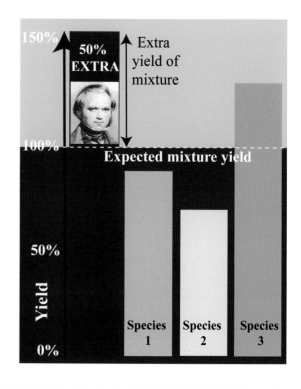

FIGURE 5.   *Darwin Effect.*

2. How mixtures enable trees to grow faster

While there are many reasons for the over-yielding effect of mixing different species, it has taken modern science and innumerable studies to understand the contribution of the countless components involved.

a. Canopy patterns

In a forest context, rugosity – surface roughness – refers to the degree of unevenness of a canopy's outline. Species-rich tree mixtures have a more uneven outline than monocultures because their canopies are denser and more complex and individual trees grow to different heights. It has been recently shown that rugosity (a complex of different factors summarising the variability in the vertical and horizontal distribution and density of forest vegetation)[5] is the single most important factor related to the increased growth of tree mixtures. 83% of the primary productivity of a forest in terms of carbon storage can be accounted for by canopy rugosity (Figure 6).[5] The more complex the upper layers

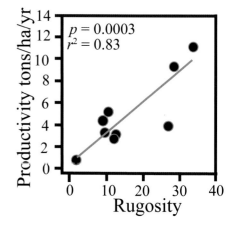

FIGURE 6.

Relationship between canopy rugosity and productivity for a range of forests ([5] see permissions p161).

of a forest, the greater the amount of the sun's energy that is trapped. Mixed species canopies (Figure 7) are far more complex than the surface monolayers found in monocultures (Figure 8). Different species in complex forests benefit from variations in tree height, overlapping branches (Figure 9), leaf size, light requirements and structure[6] so that canopy closure is earlier, indicating faster growth rates, and greater total biomass.[7]

FIGURE 7.
Complex canopy in a tropical jungle with multiple species.

FIGURE 8.
Single canopy layer in a monoculture of spruce.

b. Root overlap

Woodlands with multiple species are also characterised by greater complexity below ground (Figure 9).[7] Root overlap means that more parts of the soil are accessed leading to increased water and nutrient usage. For example, deep-rooted trees raise water when upper soils are dry. This hydraulic uplift benefits shallow-rooted neighbours, particularly during droughts.[8] Furthermore, symbiotic relationships, the complex beneficial interactions between different organisms, are improved. Consequently, there are fewer root infections (see soil pathogens below).

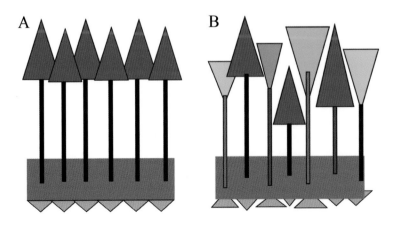

FIGURE 9.
Less overlap of branches and roots in a monoculture (A) compared with a mixture (B).

c. Overlapping annual growth periods

Different trees have different growth periods so competition for resources is spread throughout the year. Some such as conifers and eucalypts grow all year round, whereas deciduous trees only grow in warmer periods when they have leaves. Even then, understory deciduous trees may take advantage of the low light levels to make growth in spring and autumn periods when canopy trees are leafless (Figure 10).

FIGURE 10.

Growth of different tree types in temperate climates.

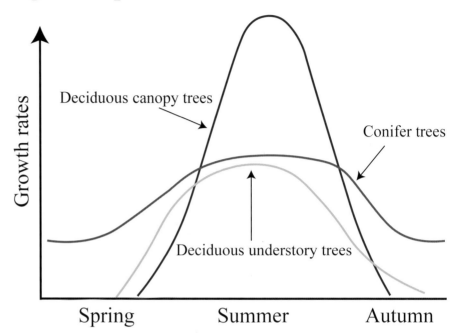

d. Reduced infection rates

Trees are dependent on hugely complex 'immune systems' to survive. This is hardly surprising since oak trees, for example, have to stand their ground against innumerable bacteria, fungi, caterpillars and aphids for perhaps 1,000 years. If they had no capacity to defend themselves, every tree would be dead within weeks – just as humans would be.

A few of their immune defence mechanisms have been identified, but most are still unknown. One example, which can be readily observed, is that many caterpillars rarely consume any one leaf completely. As they start eating a small tasty area, their saliva quickly triggers the release of unpleasant or harmful chemicals in adjacent areas and neighbouring leaves, making them unpalatable, so the caterpillars stop eating and move elsewhere (Figure 11).

In monocultures, predators and infections spread quickly since there is a massive supply of similar food. The Irish Potato Famine (1845-52) is an example where the potato blight fungus decimated a single variety of potato crop. In contrast, in species-rich mixtures, target species are diluted out among many

▲ **FIGURE 11.**

Caterpillar eating tasty parts of a leaf.

others so it is harder for diseases to spread.[9-11] This effect applies to many kinds of pathogens, predators and herbivores. Figure 12A compares diversity of plants (each square represents a mixture) with pathogen diversity and overall infection rates. Species diversity in mixtures is associated with more pathogens (each may have its own particular infectious agent) but there are lower overall infection rates (Figure 12B). Infections continue to fall with increasing numbers of plant species per mixture. Monocultures are thus far more prone to diseases (Figure 13), a problem that is particularly relevant to the UK forestry industry. Evidence shows that ash dieback is worse in pure ash plantations, as is *Phytophthora* fungus in larch and red band needle blight in pine.

An example of this effect at Norbury is shown in Figure 14. A pure Douglas fir plantation became infested with woolly aphids (*Adelges cooleyi*) while a lone Douglas fir tree in a nearby mixed species woodland was completely unaffected. Moreover, specific tree species or tree combinations may be important for reducing infections in mixtures. In our mixed species woodlands, we found that ash dieback was less frequent in ash trees with Scots pine as neighbours but was more frequent in ash trees with alders as neighbours.[13]

When trees are infected, they switch their resources to fighting the disease and as a result their growth rates slow down. Since trees in monocultures are more readily infected than tree mixtures, they tend to be smaller and store less carbon.

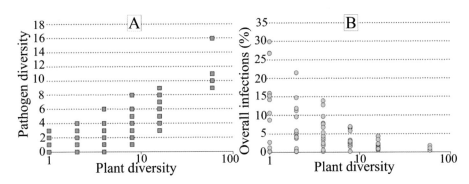

FIGURE 12. *There are more pathogens with increasing species mixtures (A) but they cause fewer infections (B) ([10] see permissions p161).*

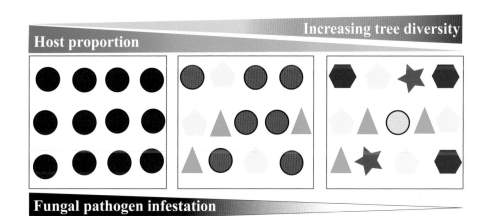

FIGURE 13. *Increasing tree diversity reduces fungal infections as target trees are diluted in a mixture.[12]*

FIGURE 14. *Woolly aphids on Douglas fir trees in (A) a monoculture of Douglas fir and (B) in a neighbouring mixed species plantation.*

> "
> The fungal wood wide web transfers water, carbon, nutrients and minerals between plants.
> "

e. Soil pathogens

Whatever is seen above ground in terms of infections and growth rates is mirrored underground but with massively more complexity since there are millions of soil organisms at play. Some studies claim that the over-yielding of mixtures can largely be explained by soil pathogens depressing productivity more in low- than in high-diversity plant communities.[14] However, as can be seen from other studies on the benefits of complex mixtures, it is unlikely that soil pathogens are the only cause of reduced growth rates in monocultures.

Because of their inaccessibility, far less is known about soil organisms than above-ground organisms. For example, a cross-linked network of fungal hyphae, rather appealingly called the 'wood wide web', links the root hairs of different tree species. How this and other underground organisms help or harm tree growth and survival is not well understood.

f. Help from neighbours

While many defence mechanisms are for the sole benefit of the particular tree that is infected, other mechanisms have a 'help-thy-neighbour' effect. For instance, chemicals released into the air by certain tree species under aphid attack can attract predatory ladybirds. This not only benefits the trees releasing the chemicals but also adjacent trees that may not have a similar defence mechanism but are also infected (Figure 15).

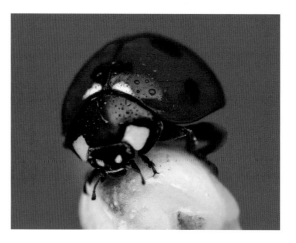

◀ **FIGURE 15.**
A helping hand.

g. Nitrogen fixation

The growth rates of many forests are restricted by low nitrogen concentrations. This element is an essential part of protein molecules without which life is impossible. Inevitably, lack of nitrogen leads to low plant growth rates and death while additional nitrogen improves growth rates and plant health. Adding artificial nitrogen fertilisers may be possible on wheat or potato crops but it is impossible in forests because of their size and the costs. This has led to nitrogen-fixing tree species being added into tree mixtures. (Nitrogen-fixing trees have bacterial nodules on their roots that convert atmospheric nitrogen into soluble nitrates that can be metabolised.)

In a 70-year-long experiment on nitrogen-poor soils, Douglas fir trees almost doubled their stem mass per hectare when mixed with nitrogen-fixing red alder compared with a pure plantation containing no alder trees (Figure 16).[15] Other studies have shown the growth benefits of adding nitrogen-fixing trees to eucalyptus and walnut plantations.[16,17] Furthermore, phosphate, another essential tree growth factor, is scavenged from deep soils by nitrogen-fixing trees, thus adding further to their fertilising effects.[18]

In the future, it may be very important to include nitrogen-fixing trees in new woodlands. UK soils tend to be low in nitrates and since trees grow faster with higher CO_2 levels, soils will become further nitrogen-depleted which in turn will limit tree growth (see Chapter 2 and Chapter 6).

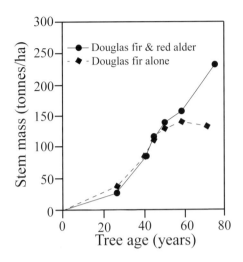

▲ **FIGURE 16.**

Douglas fir growth when mixed with Red alder.[15]

h. Being in the right place: neighbours, microclimate and luck

Mixed woodlands, helpful neighbours, advantageous genes, a place in the sun, no diseases and a slice of luck may provide the right combination of factors that help individual trees grow quickly; some fortunate combination of nature and nurture. Perhaps a young tree is planted in a particularly nutritious area of soil which provides a little extra growth; its growing tip receives extra sunlight so its enlarging canopy expands over its neighbours. It may avoid a few damaging infections that slow its competitors and soon it is the largest tree in its grove. The massive complexity of mixed woodlands with their innumerable organisms precludes a full understanding of all the factors that might be working favourably for an individual tree. However, what is clear from the scientific literature is that complex tree mixtures are important for high growth rates for the woodland as a whole. The logical consequence of these observations is to retain all tree species when thinning woodlands so that high growth rates are maintained throughout the life cycle of the winning trees (see Chapter 2: halo-pollarding).

3. The effects of faster tree growth rates on timber quality and tree age

a. Higher quality timber for some trees but not all

Timber is judged to be of good quality if it is straight grained, contains few knots and is strong. The latter component depends in part upon the amount of hollow water-conducting tissue (xylem tubes) of an individual tree species. Strong wood contains less xylem tubes than weak wood and this depends upon the growth period of the year. In spring, all trees start producing xylem to conduct water from their roots to the growing branches and young leaves. Conifer trees produce thin xylem tubes throughout the year with rather more in the summer (Figure 17). Trees such as beech and alder (diffuse porous), produce large tubes throughout the year whereas trees such as oak and ash (ring porous) produce very large tubes in early spring and smaller ones during the rest of the growing season.

When trees grow faster, it is only the summer wood that increases in thickness. Since the summer wood of oak and ash (ring porous) has fewer and smaller xylem tubes, it is stronger than earlywood. Hence,

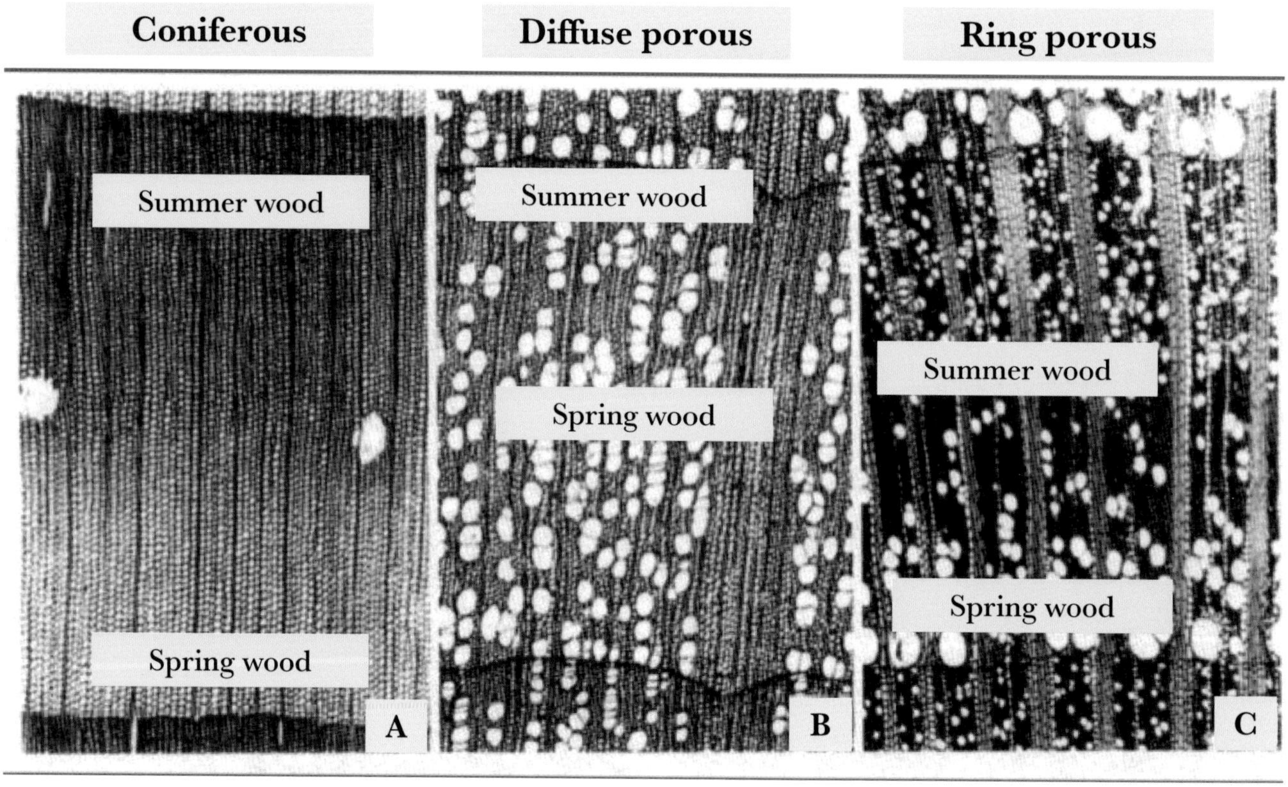

| **Coniferous** | **Diffuse porous** | **Ring porous** |

▲ **FIGURE 17.**   *Magnified cross-section of one annual growth ring in conifer, diffuse porous and ring porous trees.*[19]

oak and ash timber is stronger in fast growing trees. In contrast, the strength of beech and alder is unaffected since the proportion of wood-weakening tubes is the same throughout the year. On the other hand, increased summer growth weakens conifer timber because the latewood contains more water-conducting tubes.

It is often claimed that timber from oak trees that have grown slowly is stronger than timber from trees that have grown quickly, but in fact, the opposite is true. Faster growth produces stronger oak timber.

b. Grow faster – die younger

Trees that grow fast beyond their juvenile seedling-sapling stage commonly burn themselves out whereas slower growing individuals survive longer.[20] For example, very slow growing trees such as the Bristle comb pine found in arid, cold climates live for thousands of years. This has led to suggestions that in the higher CO_2 environments of the future, trees will have faster growth rates and die sooner, and so will store carbon for shorter periods. However, since regrowth will also be faster and harvesting could be earlier, there may be benefits from shorter life-spans in managed woodlands.

4. How many different tree species should be planted in mixed woodlands?

My answer is as many as possible – the more the better, and not just native broadleaves or conifer mixtures. A mix and match approach (with the correct advice from foresters – naturally) because these combinations will grow faster and be more resistant to infections and climate change than limited species mixtures.

Trees from other temperate zones such as Europe, USA, the Far East and the southern continents should be included. In our mixed plantations we have typically planted between 20 and 30 species, many from the USA and the Far East.

Arguments for planting only native UK species in a changing climate on the basis that they are better for the environment are flawed. It is only by chance that the UK has a mere 32 native species (46 if all closely related sub-species are included). These are the few that have re-colonised our islands after they were scoured clean during the last Ice Age. While they have adapted well to past climates, they are not well adapted to hotter, drier and the more infectious environments that are being predicted.

It is unfortunate for tree diversity in Northern Europe that the great mountain ranges of Europe run east-west (Figure 18). After the ice caps destroyed forests in Northern Europe, it took thousands of years for tree seeds from warmer Mediterranean regions to cross the mountain barriers of the Pyrenees, Alps and Carpathians to re-colonise lands to the north. In contrast, North

American mountain ranges run north-south and this allowed trees to re-establish themselves more easily as ice sheets receded. In South-East Asia there are even fewer barriers to species mixing. Consequently, in the whole of Europe there are 454 species of trees, while North America has over 1,000 and China 4,672. This compares with 60,000 in the whole world, mostly in the tropics which have been unaffected by the Ice Ages and species have been mixing and competing for tens of millions of years.

If evolution had unlimited time, and all possible temperate climate tree species were allowed to mix, what would the UK tally be? Perhaps 300 different species per hectare as in the Amazon.

It is therefore only reasonable but also sensible that non-native species should be added to new woodland mixtures when Forestry Commission grant support is being requested. As the woodland grows, the best performing species can be retained, or perhaps exotic trees removed to leave a native woodland. A wide range of species in the initial mixture keeps woodland management options open for many years and may benefit carbon storage in a changing climate.

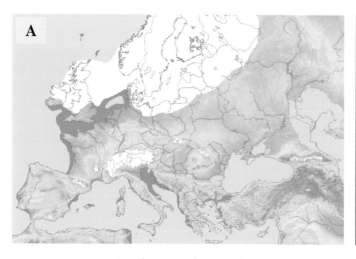 

▲ **FIGURE 18.** *Ice sheets and mountain ranges in Europe (A) and North America (B).*

Mixed conifer and broad leaf woodland. ▷

Conclusion

In a monoculture, each and every tree is surrounded by identical neighbours competing with them directly for light and nutrients and exposed to the same pathogens and herbivores. Trees with different neighbour species are using different strategies to compete for the same resources of sunlight, water or nutrients while predators and infections are diluted out and become less common. As a result, trees in mixtures grow faster and store more carbon. It is logical, therefore, to retain the species mixtures throughout the life cycle of the woodlands.

Chapter 4

Renewable energy: timber, fire logs, woodchip and solar power

There's more to woodland management than merely planting trees

When we first purchased Norbury Park Estate, our focus was almost entirely on planting trees. We gave little thought to felling them, apart from a few to sustain our woodstoves (Chapter 2). I even felled some myself! But we soon realised that in order to sustain our existing woodlands and ensure healthy new ones, we needed to manage them actively, a process that would require skilled staff. The question was: how could we best achieve this to optimise carbon sequestration?

We soon realised that carbon sequestration in trees does not stop when they are felled. Timber beams, floor boards in buildings and furniture can store wood-based carbon for potentially hundreds of years. Furthermore, although burning fire logs and woodchip release CO_2 into the atmosphere, at least we have sequestered it first. By comparison, no CO_2 sequestration occurs with the burning of fossil fuels such as coal, oil and gas for heating and electricity generation.

Although forest management is frequently carried out by contractors, we thought we should be actively involved at each stage. This would enable us to fully understand what was involved and optimise the outcomes rather than lose control to others.

Our 180 acres of mature and semi-mature woodlands contain thousands of trees. These include nearly 3,000 oaks more than 150 years old (Figure 1) plus ash, beech, sycamore, larch and many other species. One of the first jobs was to remove dying trees and those in the understory that had grown poorly – several hundred in total.

Just to move timber butts weighing several tonnes required a large tractor and trailer, plus chainsaws, jacks, wedges and protective clothing. I started the tree felling with assistance from a friend (Figures 1–3), a borrowed tractor and a rented mobile wood-mill. It was great fun learning how to drop a tree straight and true (although the occasional one did fall in the opposite direction). Thankfully, I still have my fingers.

After a relatively inexpensive start and extensive reading about selling planks and fire logs, we realised we would need to dry the timber ourselves. In 2012, we invested in a large drying shed. It was designed to be large enough for all our planned timber stacks, huge piles of fire logs and heaps of woodchip

◁ **FIGURE 1.**

Felling a 160-year-old oak tree.

FIGURE 2.

My first attempt at starting a chainsaw!

(Figures 4, 14 and 18). Next on the list was a timber mill. We chose a large Mebor bandsaw (HTZ 1200 SP) from Slovenia with a 13-metre bed so that we could cut the very longest of logs (Figure 5).

The first uses of the timber were for renovating properties on the estate, several of which were in need of attention. Our emphasis was on the production of green-oak beams (Figure 6), high quality, quarter-sawn boards (from logs cut through the middle as in Figure 7) and wood-cladding (Figure 8), with the tree residue converted to fire logs and woodchip.

As the estate had no history of selling timber – or indeed any type of wood product – we needed to

gain commercial experience. After a couple of years of preparation and careful drying of our oak and ash boards, we set up Shelmore Timber. Its purpose: to sell beams, planks and fire logs from the estate into local markets (Figure 9).

Planks for use in houses need to be dried to a water content of around 10%. Our open-sided drying shed could reduce the water content to 15-18% (from 50-60% in freshly felled timber) but only a wood kiln could dry it further.

Initially, we sent our timber elsewhere for drying but this was expensive, with high transport costs, so we commissioned a kiln of our own. Our computer-controlled Shelmore Timber kiln

FIGURE 3.

Trimming a felled tree trunk.

FIGURE 4.

Stacked planks in the drying shed.

FIGURE 5.

Mebor HTZ 1200 SP bandsaw.

has a capacity of 1,000 cu ft, is heated by a woodchip boiler using our own fuel and has a cycle time of 2–3 weeks for one load (Figure 10). Different woods can be dried together, providing they have similar characteristics, but since most of our timber is oak, this dominates the kiln's use.

After a few years of low sales, in 2018 we appointed Ian McFarlane as sales director. Since then, sales have grown enormously (Figure 11). Ian came to us with 40 years' experience in the timber trade and knew all the significant customers and wood product producers in the UK.

In fact, his sales success has been so good that it has outstripped the timber supplies from our own woods. As a result, we are now buying wood-lots from around the UK to supplement our own. In addition, we are complementing our product range with hardwood from the USA and a limited range of tropical timbers (Figure 12), all with green credentials (FSC registered) in terms of their sustainable harvesting.

FIGURE 6.

(Left) Green oak beams on Shelmore Lodge extension.

FIGURE 7.

(Right) Quarter-sawn oak boards.

FIGURE 8.

Sweet chestnut cladding on a bat barn.

FIGURE 9.

Shelmore Timber brochure.

FIGURE 10.

Ian McFarlane, with dried boards in the kiln.

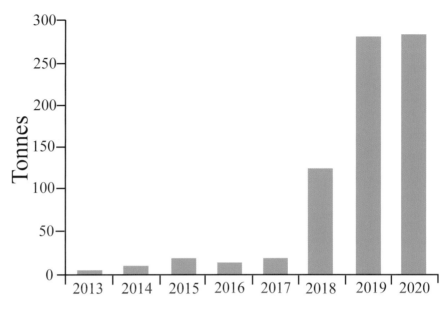

FIGURE 11. *Annual timber sales.*

FIGURE 12.

17-tonne West African sipo log arriving from Belgium.

FIGURE 13.

Fire log production.

Fire logs

Around 30-40% of a tree by volume is branch wood, which is of no use for planks and beams. However, as a renewable energy source in the form of fire logs it makes a valuable contribution to reducing fossil fuel usage.

There are two main requirements for good fire logs: they need to be the right size for wood stoves and they must be thoroughly dried. Moisture content should be under 20% so they burn cleanly without the production of polluting smoke. Indeed, the Government banned the sale of wet fire logs in February 2021 (in volumes less than two cubic metres). Even fully dried, logs are not recommended for open fires as they produce far too much smoke and most of the heat goes up the chimney.

Cutting small volumes of logs into suitable sizes is simple – buy a small chainsaw. But this is of little use when there are hundreds of cubic metres to handle. Even with high-capacity log splitters (Figure 13), it takes weeks of work by a three-man team and there are always awkward butts that have to be cut by hand.

Storing the logs is an additional problem. Oak logs dry slowly, necessitating two years in a large well-ventilated shed (Figure 14). They need to be lifted onto the top of the piles with a conveyor and not moved until sold. Lifting them with a grab or bucket digger always generates dust and debris, reducing their quality. After several years of trial and error, we now place the logs in long bays, filling from one end and emptying from the other after two drying seasons.

The dried logs are delivered to customers in two cubic metre volumes (approximately one tonne) in a tipper truck within a seven-mile radius of the wood mill. Annual sales growth and seasonality of sales are shown in Figures 15 and 16.

As sales have expanded, there is now insufficient branch wood from our large trees. However, tree thinnings from the 180 ha of young plantations, which are up to 11 years old (Chapter 2), are starting to make a significant contribution to fire log volumes.

▲ **FIGURE 14.** *Drying fire logs.*

FIGURE 15. ▷
Fire log sales per year.

FIGURE 16. ▷
Seasonality of fire log sales shown for 2020-21.

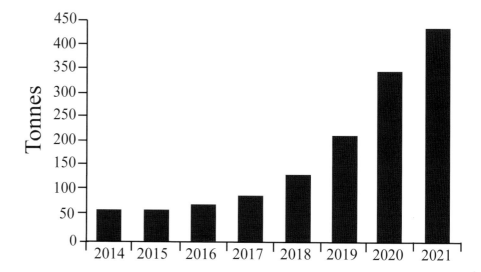

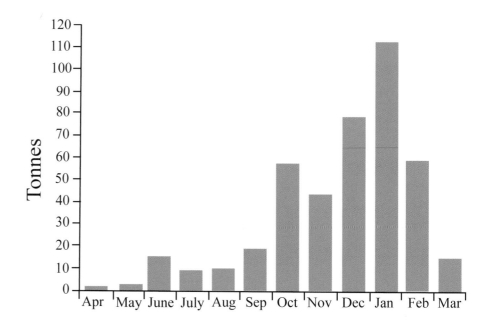

Woodchip

Branches that are too small for fire logs (less than 3-4 inches) are used to make woodchip. It is preferable to use soft wood (from conifer trees) rather than hardwood (from oak, ash, birch, etc.) because it dries more quickly. Furthermore, conifer wood is not recommended for fire logs because it burns quickly and is a fire risk when used in open grates as it has a tendency to produce sparks.

For chipping the wood, we required yet more machinery (Figure 17), plus use of the large drying shed (Figure 18) and, of course, woodchip boilers. We use three such boilers; a Herz Firematic TP 150 kW for the main estate office and surrounding buildings, a Froling TX 150 kW for the wood kiln and a Windhager PuroWIN 60 kW for the Shelmore Timber showroom and its adjacent arboriculture training centre (Chapter 9). The woodchip is dried alongside the fire logs and is ready for use in a few weeks. Estate usage is approximately 150 cubic metres per year and any excess is sold.

▲ **FIGURE 17.**
Woodchip production.

▲ **FIGURE 18.**
Woodchip drying.

> " Conifer wood is not recommended for fire logs because it burns quickly and is a fire risk when used in open grates. "

Carbon offset with solar power

Other widely used sources of renewable energy are wind and solar power. Wind turbines are very efficient and, of course, can turn at night when there is no sunlight, but they are huge installations with a high visual impact and are generally resisted by the public. A local farmer had tried to install three large wind turbines but the plan was opposed by horrified villagers in Norbury. This dissuaded us from a similar idea. In contrast, solar photovoltaic (PV) panels have little environmental impact, are easy to install, and are surprisingly efficient even on cloudy days. Since the roofs of our woodsheds face south, they are ideal locations for solar panel arrays. Furthermore, we built the woodsheds with asymmetrical roofs in order to provide larger south-facing surfaces

(Figure 19).

Over six years, we have gradually increased the installed capacity from an initial 345 m² to 710 m² and recently to a total of 1,439 m², producing 235 kW at maximum sun intensity. Total production to date has been 735 MW and we can now generate 270,000 kWh per year. As the average UK electricity consumption is 3,700 kWh per household per year, we are generating enough to power 75 homes, about the same usage as the whole of nearby Norbury village. Inevitably, most of the electricity is produced in the summer months (Figure 20), but even in other months, there is often sufficient power for the bandsaw, electric tools and a forklift truck. Although in winter we have to import electricity from The Western

⏶ **FIGURE 19.**

Solar panels on a lopsided shed roof.

Power Distribution grid to satisfy our needs, in summer we export it to provide a good revenue.

Of the power we generated in 2020 (with only the first 710 m² array), we used 61% and exported 39%. Of the total power we consumed, 42% was from our solar panels (range: January 7%; May 71%) while 58% was imported. The expansion to the full 235 kW array in 2021 might even produce enough electricity in the dark winter months for most of our internal use in the sawmill and elsewhere.

It is of interest to compare the efficiency and cost of generating power from woodland and solar panels. Thus, 1 kg of dried wood, of around 15% moisture content, yields 4.2 kWh of energy. This is independent of the type of wood since all wood is similar chemically, although dense logs obviously contain more energy per cubic metre. Since a typical woodland accumulates approximately 10 tonnes of wood per hectare per year (10,000

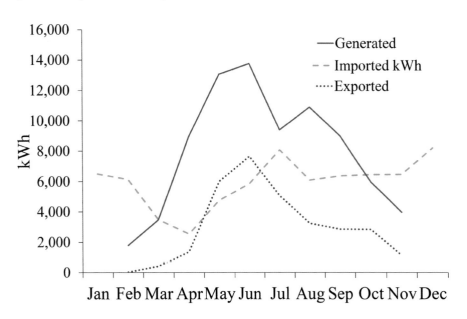

⏶ **FIGURE 20.**   *Seasonal solar power generation and usage in 2020.*

m²), one square metre accumulates 1 kg per year – which yields 4.2 kWh of stored energy.

In contrast, a solar panel with 20% efficiency and an area of one sq metre will produce 185 kWh per year (under standard test conditions, one 1,000 kWh is equivalent to 317 kg of CO_2). Hence, solar panels are 58-fold more productive than woodland. However, they are also much more expensive. One hectare of woodland costs £10,000 to plant and manage, with typical lowland land costs of £20,000 per ha in 2020, whereas one hectare of roof-installed solar panels costs around £1.4m, 47 times more expensive. Hence, per kWh of energy produced, woodland and solar panels cost about the same (solar panels are 58-fold more productive but 47 times as expensive). It may be cheaper to install panels on grassland than on the roofs of buildings but this incurs a loss of use as pasture or arable land. It seems, therefore, that there is no obvious economic reason to favour one over the other and both have the potential to contribute to reduced fossil fuel usage.

The contribution of Shelmore Timber to carbon sequestration

In Chapter 2 we calculated the amounts of carbon that we are locking up in our woodlands – around 3,000 tonnes per year and increasing as the trees grow larger. When trees are removed and converted to beams, planks or furniture, the carbon is locked up for another 50 years or more. By using timber in estate properties, we have a lower carbon footprint than by incorporating other building materials such as steel, concrete or plastics.

In comparison, fire-log and woodchip combustion returns the carbon to the atmosphere, making the process essentially carbon neutral. The CO_2 is collected from the atmosphere by the trees for perhaps 100 years then returned within a year or two as the wood fuel is burnt. This is of benefit as it offsets the use of fossil fuels but is not reducing the amount of CO_2 in the atmosphere; only sequestering the carbon in growing the trees can do that.

Solar PV is different again. There is a small CO_2 footprint in their manufacture and a little more from their installation while their benefit is to reduce generation of electricity from fossil fuels. It takes around six months for a solar PV panel to generate the energy required to balance the CO_2 emitted during its production, after that it provides a carbon offset (Figure 21). Overall, such power sources have remarkably low fossil CO_2 emissions during their productive lifetimes compared with power stations burning fossil fuels (Table 1).

Fuel type	CO₂ production
Natural gas	200 g/kWh
Coal	340 g/kWh
Nuclear	4 g/kWh
Solar	6 g/kWh
Wind	4 g/kWh
Fire logs	2 g/kWh

▲ TABLE 1.

Fossil CO_2 emissions in grams from different power sources per kWh of electricity production during their lifetimes.

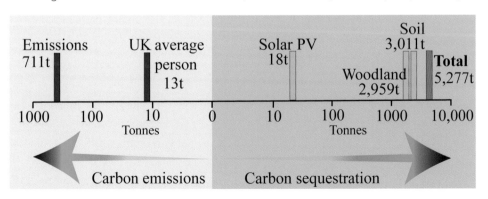

▲ **FIGURE 21.** *Contribution of solar PV to Carbon sequestration at Norbury Park in 2020.*

What guidance are we offering to others?

▷ *Oaks in Shelmore Wood*

We have taken a holistic view on carbon sequestration: from planting trees to processing them into timber, fire logs and wood chip, then adding large installations of solar PV panels for electricity production. We have described our experience, not necessarily intending for others to follow, but rather to show why and how we have tried to maximise our carbon reduction in the woodlands and timber business. Many large estates in the UK are able to plant woodlands, but few would be interested in processing the resulting timber or fire logs. For us it has been a journey of discovery and interest, which is enough in itself. We fully realise that we are in an unusual and fortunate financial position. Nevertheless, it is also a matter of scale. We are all being encouraged to reduce our carbon footprint. Many can plant trees in their gardens or buy small woods and process the timber for their own pleasure: anyone with a suitable roof can install solar panels while everyone can potentially use wood products rather than plastics if the choice is available.

▽ **FIGURE 22.**
Shelmore Timber team. Lt to Rt: Dan Hawkins, Steve Watkin, Mick Camplejohn, Chris Smith, Alec Taylor, Arron Ashley and Ian McFarlane

Chapter 5

Farming a revolution – carbon storage on arable land

Ploughs, worms and the Darwin Effect

As we have seen, trees store carbon in their trunks: one cubic metre of timber contains the equivalent of one tonne of CO_2 (Chapter 2). A large oak tree might weigh more than ten tonnes so, at perhaps 50 trees per hectare, this equates to 500 tonnes of stored CO_2. In addition, carbon is present in leaf litter, roots, worms, insects and debris, providing a further 150 tonnes per hectare of carbon in woodland.

Farmland also contains a store of carbon. It is hidden in the soil, yet integral to its proper functioning. High-quality fertile land might contain 8% carbon in the form of soil organic matter. Taken down to a depth of 50 cm, this translates into 400 tonnes per hectare.

Healthy soils with a high carbon content have an extensive network of porous structures which allows water, air and nutrients to circulate. When carbon is lost from the soil, these pores become smaller and less connected. Water and nutrients circulate more slowly, which leads to reduced growth. Manure is high in carbon and nitrogen, whereas manufactured fertilisers containing

nitrates are devoid of carbon. Consequently, decades of applying manufactured fertilisers have starved soils of carbon.

Poor quality soils might contain only 2-3% carbon. These are the soils that have been exhausted because of over-farming, a feature typical of much arable farmland in the UK. Since the farmed area in England is more than twice that of

woodland, replenishing soil carbon would have a large impact on the UK's obligations to offset CO_2 emissions by 2050.

Farmland makes up 32% of the Norbury Park Estate and has a typical carbon content of 2.5%. To improve its carbon storage and fertility, we have re-sown it over several stages and introduced new management regimens.

How and why did the UK's farmland become carbon-depleted?

Farmers have always tried to boost crop production by adding nitrogen fertilisers to their soils. This has ranged from the traditional cattle manure, to guano from Pacific Ocean islands and, for the past 100 years, nitrates produced by the Haber–Bosch process; this converts atmospheric nitrogen into ammonia which is then used to make nitrates. After World War II, the use of manufactured nitrogen fertilisers intensified because they were cheap. Armament factories lost their markets for nitrogen-based explosives, so they adapted their chemical processes to make cut-price nitrates. These were applied to crops for continuous food production, replacing traditional

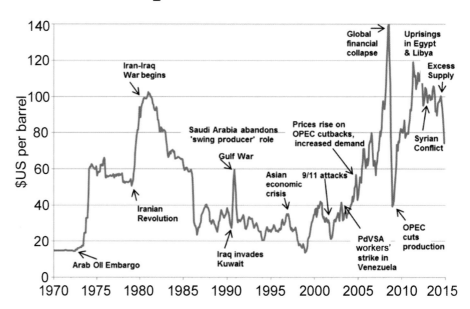

▲ FIGURE 1. *Oil price shocks have increased fertiliser costs (at constant 2013 $US prices) and hence crop production costs since 1974.*

cropland rotation whereby fields were left uncultivated for one year in four to be grazed by cattle or sheep.

Unfortunately, fertiliser manufacturing processes rely on high temperatures, requiring huge amounts of gas or oil with high CO_2 emissions. Then, in the 1970s, shock oil price rises dramatically increased fertiliser costs (Figure 1). This forced farmers to become more efficient by amalgamating or enlarging fields and planting larger single-species crops. But this only led to further costs resulting from increasing wage bills, larger machinery and rising interest repayments on bank loans. In addition, larger single-crop areas meant more pests and diseases, leading to the use of expensive pesticides, herbicides and fungicides. Genetic development of crops for disease resistance further added to costs and debts. This vicious cycle led to reduced profits, more subsidies and, as carbon stocks became depleted through over-farming, declining soil health. This has been the unfortunate consequence of the so-called Green Revolution.

In recent times, the approach championed by HRH Charles, Prince of Wales – reverting to the old ways, going organic and reducing use of fertilisers – is finally gaining ground. This is brilliantly explained in David Montgomery's book *Growing a Revolution – Bringing our soils back to life*.[1] Using numerous examples, he shows that a return to field-rotation farming using fewer chemicals and

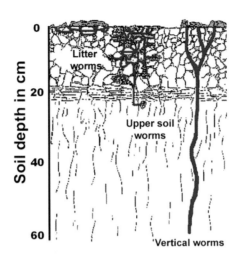

Diagram courtesy of the Science Learning Hub. Figure adapted from Fraser and Boag,

FIGURE 2.

Different habitats of worms.

the latest discoveries of soil science restores land fertility and productivity while increasing carbon storage.

There has been another long-term disaster for soil carbon retention. Surprisingly, perhaps, this is ploughing. It is often said that the plough was the cornerstone of human advancement from hunter-gathering to agriculture. Indeed so, because ploughing turns over the uppermost soil, bringing fresh nutrients to the surface, while at the same time burying weeds and allowing crop remnants to decay. But ploughing has two deleterious effects: the soil slowly migrates downhill or is blown away in strong winds; and it kills worms.

The soils of ancient Greece, the Italian peninsula, North Africa and the Middle East used to be highly fertile. Gradually, with each turn of the plough, a little more soil moved

downhill to be washed away in rain storms and floods until not much remained. The very countries that were once the bread baskets of the ancient world are now dry and barren.

Killing worms is the other great downside of ploughing. Some worm species process litter or soil on the surface while others burrow to greater depths (Figure 2). None survive well when they are turned over or cut into pieces by ploughs. As Charles Darwin pointed out as long ago as 1881, worms are a huge asset to soils and soil structure (Figure 3).[2] Over a season, if present in adequate numbers, they ingest and process 25 tonnes of soil per hectare, enriching it, enhancing plant growth and helping drainage. A healthy soil is full of worms; an overploughed field is devoid of worms. Ploughing should be done by worms, not ploughs!

THE FORMATION

OF

VEGETABLE MOULD,

THROUGH THE

ACTION OF WORMS,

WITH

OBSERVATIONS ON THEIR HABITS.

By CHARLES DARWIN, LL.D., F.R.S.

FIGURE 3.

Title page of Darwin's 1882 worm book.

Love Your Earthworms

(courtesy of Cotswold Seeds):[3]

'Earthworms are indicators of soil health. They oxygenate soil and eat soil, thereby playing a huge role in returning carbon to the soil (because the soil contains more living and hence dead organisms). Intensive farming, frequent tillage, pesticide use, artificial fertilisers and unavailability of manures/compost have all contributed to declines in soil organic matter and soil health and ultimately declines in earthworm populations. This, in turn, has impacted on the many species of wildlife which eat earthworms including lapwing, curlew, buzzards and even foxes! Did you know it's even thought that worms may interact and form herds? Earthworm casts contain five times more nitrogen, seven times more phosphorous, 11 times more potash, and 1.5 times more calcium than surrounding soils.

Cultivation systems such as 'minimum-tillage' and 'zero-tillage' tend to reduce the loss of earthworms. Compacted soil reduces earthworm mobility, impedes crop root growth and in turn leads to increased risk of soil run-off during heavy rainfall. Run-off takes with it soil and nutrients such as phosphate so that watercourses clog up, aquatic plant growth is suppressed, oxygenation is reduced and fish are robbed of spawning habitats.

Look after your earthworms and they will look after you.'

We fully agree with this sentiment. Solutions to soil degeneration and worm preservation are to directly drill plant seeds into the soil and to revert to crop rotations or fallow land, with nitrogen fertilisation provided by bacteria associated with clover.

At Norbury, the arable land had been intensely farmed for 40 years to grow wheat, barley, oats, potatoes and oilseed rape. Following the science, we reverted over three separate stages to traditional farming methods.

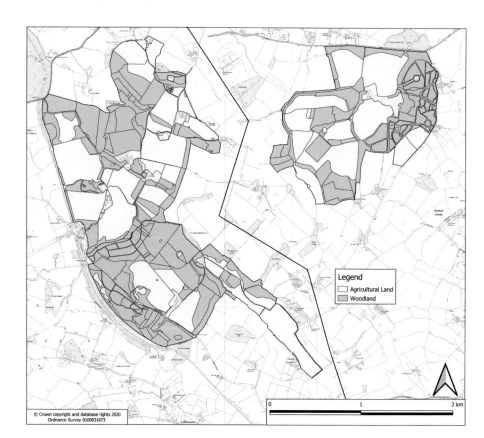

FIGURE 4. ▷

Location of 190 ha of agricultural land at Norbury Park.

Stage 1. From arable crops to grass leys with clover

At Norbury, our 160 ha of arable land (out of a total of 190 ha of agricultural land) (Figure 4) had an average carbon content of only 2.5% (ideally it should be around 8%). It was contaminated with nematode worms from potato crops and had excess water run-off because of poor soil drainage. Furthermore, because of insecticide use, there were few beneficial insects or bees.

In 2016, with the tenant farmer retiring, we decided that the fields needed resting from intensive cultivation. Realising that we could sell silage to several surrounding dairy farms, we decided to plant fast-growing ryegrass and clover (Appendix 8). During August/September 2016, the arable fields were treated with herbicide (Roundup) to clear crop remnants then ploughed, power-harrowed, heavy-rolled and sown with the grass and clover seeds using an EinBock grass-seeding machine (Figure 5).

The following year, after adding nitrogen, phosphate and potash, the fields (Figure 6) produced three good cuts of silage. Cattle slurry and farmyard manure were applied where possible to reduce the use of manufactured fertilisers.

▲ **FIGURE 5.**
EinBock grass seeder.

▲ **FIGURE 6.**
Ryegrass and clover.

Stage 2. From ryegrass and clover to herbal leys

In 2018, after two years of the ryegrass and clover mixtures, it was apparent from studies around the world that more complex herbal leys (mixtures of grasses, legumes and herbs planted on arable land) would capture more carbon. This is well described in the Cotswold Seed Company catalogue:

'Plants capture carbon from the atmosphere and transfer it to the soil where it is utilised by the soil biology to help unlock precious nutrients which would otherwise be unavailable to the growing plants. The greater the diversity of plants in a ley, the greater the diversity of soil biology which in turn produces greater yields and therefore more carbon captured. Carbon is also very important for soil structure and because of its microporous structure just a small increase in soil carbon content can have a huge impact on its ability to hold moisture. This of course is very important in times of drought. Healthy soil biology also reduces the need for artificial fertiliser derived from oil and gas, saving money and using up less of the earth's natural resources.

160 years ago, Charles Darwin in his book *On the Origin of Species* noted what happened when different grasses were grown together [see also Chapter 3].[4]

'It has been experimentally proved, that if a plot of land be sown with one species of grass, and a similar plot be sown with several distinct genera of grasses, a greater number of plants and a greater weight of dry herbage can be raised in the latter than in the former case.'

'You might assume that the potential average yield from, say, three different plants could be calculated by simply adding up the yield of each

and dividing by three. But that's not what happens. You get an overyielding factor – the Darwin Effect – as a result of the different species overlapping in terms of root depth, aerial growth and the timing of growth (Figure 7). For example, if ryegrass, red clover and chicory are grown together, you might expect the yield to be an average of the individual plants. But, as noted by Darwin, when plants are grown in a mixture the yield is much greater due to their overlapping structures, growth habits and soil niches.' (From 'Herbal Ley Farming System' courtesy of the Cotswold Seed Company.[3])

Modern-day research has confirmed these findings and showed that the more species in the mixture, the greater the carbon capture and the better the soils. In one study in North America, it was shown that, over 12 years, diverse grass

mixtures led to much larger increases in soil carbon levels (Figure 8).[5]

Another study showed that increasing grass species richness from 1 to 10 had twice the economic value of increasing species richness from 1 to 2.[6] Although each additional species added progressively less carbon to the soil, total carbon stored was still increasing with 16 species.

These scientific observations persuaded us to change to complex herbal leys, which would sequester more carbon in our soils. Had we realised this earlier, we might have started with herbal leys rather than first planting ryegrasses. With advice from Cotswold Seed Company, we chose 23 species (Appendix 10). Some of these are illustrated in Figure 9, which shows the differences in vegetation and root structures of different plants.

The herbal leys provided a greater range of features compared with

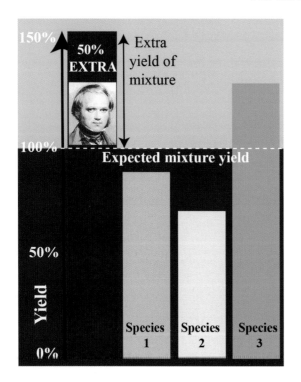

▲ **FIGURE 7.**

Darwin Effect of mixed species improving crop yields.

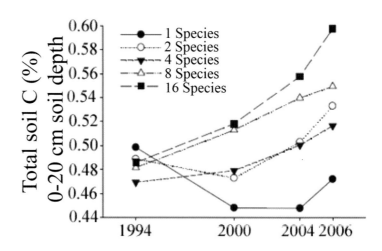

▲ **FIGURE 8.**

Increase in total carbon in soil (%) over 12 years with rising numbers of grass species ([5] see permissions p161).

our initial grass/clover mixture (Appendix 9):

a. **Nitrogen fixation:** Clovers and other legumes can add up to 250 kg of nitrogen per hectare and increase soil phosphorous levels by slowly dissolving stones from deep within the soil.

b. **Growth patterns:** Some species provide their yield early in the season while others mature later. In contrast, monocultures produce their yield in a narrower seasonal window, leaving gaps in production at other times of the year (Figure 10).

c. **Deep roots:** Plants such as sainfoin and lucerne penetrate into subsoils, increasing worm counts and humus production. This allows all species to survive better in dry periods because of hydraulic uplift of moisture deep within the soil. Furthermore, deeper drainage means less water runoff, providing flood resilience.

d. **Natural antihelmintic:** Chemicals in sainfoin, birdsfoot trefoil and chicory disrupt three main stages of the life cycle of nematode worms (roundworms) that parasitise cattle – the eggs, the larvae and the adult worms.

e. **Increased minerals:** Plants such as yarrow, plantain and burnet increase the availability of essential plant minerals such as cobalt, iodine, manganese and copper.

f. **Less weed growth:** The huge mixture in the herbal leys out-competes most weeds.

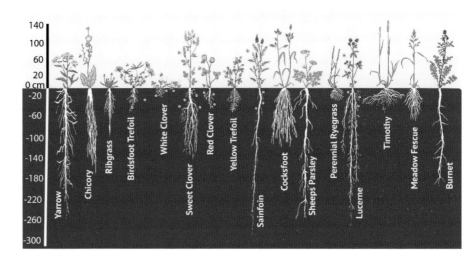

▲ **FIGURE 9.** *Herbal mixture showing 14 of the 23 planted species (appendix 10).[3]*

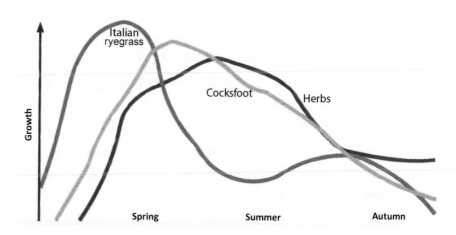

▲ **FIGURE 10.** *Growth pattern of three different herbal ley species.[3]*

> Clovers and other legumes can add up to 250 kg of nitrogen per hectare and increase soil phosphorous levels.

▲ **FIGURE 11.**

Deep roots in a complex herbal ley after a dry period.

Trial ploughing regimes, weed control and seed densities

To establish the leys, we first experimented on 16 trial plots in August 2018. We found that the best regimen was to establish the seed bed with Roundup, 8-inch-deep ploughing, power harrowing and heavy rolling. Although the worms may have been spared, plant growth was less satisfactory with no ploughing or even shallow ploughing. The seeds were spread using an Einbock seeder (Figure 5) at a density of 40 kg per ha to 1–2 cm depth, followed by a final heavy roll. With a middle to late August sowing time, we had excellent plant establishment.

By the next spring, which happened to be dry, we found that the experimental herbal ley plots had grown better than the existing ryegrass and clover plots, despite being only a few months old (Figure 11). Only ten months after planting, the herbal leys in some areas were producing 10–20% more weight of silage than three-year-old ryegrass/clover mixtures. Furthermore, when given the choice, the cattle much preferred the herbal leys over the ryegrass silage.

Having gained confidence with the experimental plots over 12 months, we planted all 160 ha of our arable land with herbal leys – more than three billion seeds.

Stage 3. From herbal leys and silage production to mob grazing

The final stage of rejuvenating our soils has been bringing in cattle from the farms that have been buying our herbal leys. Removing the herbal leys for silage three times a year and spreading cattle slurry seemed far less efficient than having the animals eat the plants on the fields. Furthermore, manure would be better for the land. Current thinking is that the technique of 'mob grazing' is better than allowing animals to browse freely.

The system involves allowing a high density of animals to graze on small plots of land but moving them every 1-3 days (Figure 12). This prevents them from overgrazing any one area while covering it evenly in manure. As they are not eaten to their bases, the plants regrow faster and develop deeper roots. What the cattle don't eat, they

trample underfoot; together with the manure, this helps feed the soil and enhance plant growth. If cattle are left to themselves on large land areas, they selectively over-graze plants they particularly like, which then struggle to regrow after being cropped to their roots.

Clearly, paddocks need careful managing as animals have to be moved more frequently. We were advised that the optimal approach is to use electric fences, with around 100 cattle on 1.25 ha fields for 2-3 days. They are repeatedly moved to adjacent fields, with a complete rotation on 10 to 15 paddocks over 32 to 48 days, depending upon plant regrowth rates.

The requirements to prepare all our 160 ha of herbal leys for mob grazing were formidable. We needed no less than 44 kilometres of electric fencing with 20 sets of batteries powered by solar panels (Figure 13) plus 54 water troughs requiring three kilometres of water pipes.

For us, mob grazing is still work in progress. We started in 2020 and plan to have cattle on all the herbal leys by spring 2022. So far we have found that the growth rates of the cattle are 0.7-1 kg/day – very good for grazing animals. Furthermore, by moving them every two to three days, we ensure they are always eating fresh food. Advantageously, the rapid field rotation is faster than the life cycle of intestinal parasites, leading to a lower cattle worm burden that is further reduced by the antihelmintic effects of the leys. The cattle certainly appear healthy and, intuitively, grazing the leys must be better than living in sheds all year round.

▲ **FIGURE 13.**

Electric fence with solar energiser.

> We have increased the carbon content of the soil by approximately 3,000 tonnes per year, similar to the carbon stored in our woodlands per year.

Environmental benefits

Mob grazing is wildlife friendly. There are no big machines compacting the land or killing small mammals, birds and frogs. All manner of insects and microbes benefit from taller plants and the fields are fertilised with proper manure instead of farmyard slurry with its minimal carbon content. However, what we don't yet know is whether the rate of carbon sequestration into the soil will increase with mob grazing compared with silage production from the herbal leys.

Calculation of carbon sequestration with grass leys and herbal leys

By ceasing the arable crops five years ago and returning the land to grass mixtures and more recently, herbal leys with cattle, we have increased the carbon content of the soil by approximately 1% to a depth of 50 cm (Appendix 10). This equates to around 3,000 tonnes per year, similar to the carbon stored in our woodlands per year (Figure 14). Adding both woodland and arable land forms of carbon sequestration together shows that we are storing nearly 6,000 tonnes of carbon per year at Norbury Park. This is offset by carbon emissions to produce a total carbon sequestration of 5,277 tonnes in 2020 (Chapter 8).

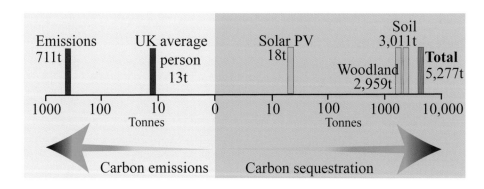

▲ **FIGURE 14.** *Contribution of the arable land soil to overall CO_2 sequestration at Norbury Park in 2020.*

Conclusion

In order to sequester more carbon in the agricultural soils at Norbury Park, we have transitioned from arable crops to grass mixtures and finally complex herbal leys with mob grazing of cattle. It has been an expensive journey. Since we started, the seeds have cost £100,000, preparing the land and sowing them £20,000, while the infrastructure for mob grazing, such as robust electric fences and water troughs, cost more than £150,000. We believe these outlays will be recouped over the years because of improved cattle health and growth rates.

We are convinced that our agricultural land is being better managed than previously. We are rejuvenating the soils, sequestering large amounts of carbon, improving cattle health and improving the environment by stopping the use of insecticides, herbicides and fungicides. Because of these known benefits, herbal leys are rapidly becoming more popular and can easily be identified by their huge variety of plant leaves and flowers.

▼ **FIGURE 15.**

Herbal leys cut for silage with the BIFoR FACE facility in the background.

Chapter 6
Pests and diseases

Oak processionary moth

Horse chestnut leaf blotch

Ash dieb[

Emerald ash borer

Agrilus beetle in acute oak decline

Dithistroma needle bli[

Asian longhorn beetle

Phytophthera ramoram

Powdery mildew on [

Elm bark beetle

Oak apple galls

Honey fun[

Fallow deer

Muntjac

Protecting our trees – and enabling them to fend for themselves

The vast majority of life on Earth depends upon plants and, of these, trees suffer more than their fair share of being eaten. They are browsed, pecked at, tunnelled-into, lived-on, stripped and digested. We fell them then turn them into furniture, houses and planks, or wood chip and burn them. Yet, despite all the abuse they receive, we now need them more than ever, to suck up all our poisonous CO_2 emissions.

> " **Plantations need to be protected from two particularly damaging animals: grey squirrels and deer.** "

We used to plant trees in monocultures so they could be processed more easily – felled and debranched with huge mechanical harvesters. Thankfully, our attachment to monocultures is waning as we are learning that trees in mixed forests grow faster and are more resilient to predators and parasites (Chapter 3). Yet even mixed plantations need to be protected from two particularly damaging animals: grey squirrels (Figure 1) and deer. Both have to be controlled vigorously by anyone owning or managing woodlands.

This chapter focuses on the animals and infections that we have experienced at Norbury Park. It is not a long list since the huge variety of our tree mixtures seems to have defeated many would-be attackers. However, since the biggest threat by far has been from grey squirrels, we have put a lot of effort into their control.

Grey squirrels

They may look cute and amusing as they play in parks and gardens, but grey squirrels are a menace. They strip the bark off oak, beech, hornbeam and sycamore trees as well as another 40 species. Wild cherry may be the only native tree species that is safe from their predations.[1] Introduced repeatedly into the UK in the late 19th century by Victorian fashion seekers, grey squirrels now threaten the very

▲ **FIGURE 1.** *Grey squirrel.*

existence of our woodlands[2,3] and native red squirrels too. They cause an estimated annual damage of £40 million to British forestry.[4] At Norbury Park, we spend more than £16,000 per year stopping them ruining our young oak woods.[5]

The grey squirrels started their attacks during the first year of planting in 2010, eating young saplings and causing apparently mindless damage. Marauding out of neighbouring woods, they bit off the leading stems – not bothering to eat them but just scattering the remnants on the ground. In our older woodlands, thousands of trees bore witness to their earlier attacks: bark stripped off beautiful maturing beech trees and huge branch damage to oaks (Figure 2). (They typically strip bark off trees aged between 10 and 40 years in spring and early summer, seeking sugars in the sap wood.[6]) In some oak coverts, the trees were so badly damaged that we wondered if any were worth keeping. We could not possibly allow that to happen to our planned third of a million trees. It was war!

Lord Lichfield's previous gamekeepers had resorted to trapping and poisoning with warfarin, but this has been outlawed as it kills other animals. The options for us were drey-poking and shooting in the winter or trapping through spring and summer. Adopting a policy of zero tolerance, we chose to do both.

We started with several dozen single-catch, live-cage traps placed

▲ **FIGURE 2.** *Old damage to maturing trees.*

in mature woodlands. After a period of experimentation, we changed to Kania 2000 bolt-action traps, which kill the squirrels outright.[7] Over a six-week period in April/May 2016, we compared 42 live-cage traps with 56 of the new Kania traps.

The cage traps caught 153 squirrels (averaging 3.6 per trap), 11 wood pigeons, six jays, four pheasants and a cat. In contrast, the Kania 2000 traps caught 273 squirrels (averaging 4.9 per trap) and one rat. This encouraged us to increase the number of Kania traps to 112 and cease the use of live-cage traps.

After further testing, Kania traps were set horizontally on raised wooden platforms (to avoid badger interference) and baited with whole maize so that bait was clearly visible (Figure 3). This method was approximately four times more effective than attaching the traps vertically to tree trunks.

▲ **FIGURE 3.** *Baited Kania trap.*

During February through May 2016, we targeted the resident squirrel population. Traps were set in mature woods, well within the estate boundaries, where squirrels were likely to be feeding (Figure 4). Obvious positions were sunny southern edges, in and around hazel thickets, and along natural travel corridors and woodland bottlenecks. A total of 260 platforms were placed across the entire woodlands. At different times, platforms were baited for 1-2 weeks to encourage feeding before the traps were deployed. Once the squirrel population had been reduced in one area, attention was moved to another.

Figure 5 shows the results of our endeavours, with an average of 541 animals culled per year over 10 years. Monthly figures for 2016-20 are shown in Figure 6. Large numbers of squirrels were caught each April, May and June, averaging 175, 142 and 152 respectively across all five years, compared with an average of 23 in July. As the resident populations were suppressed (end of May to early June), we focused on controlling the influx of squirrels from outside the estate, with most traps placed on the outer boundaries. This explains why the numbers remained high into June, even though the resident populations had been culled in May. Outside these months, the squirrels are not a threat to the trees since they have ample natural food. In addition, shooting was carried out for several days each year during December, January and February, with 30-60

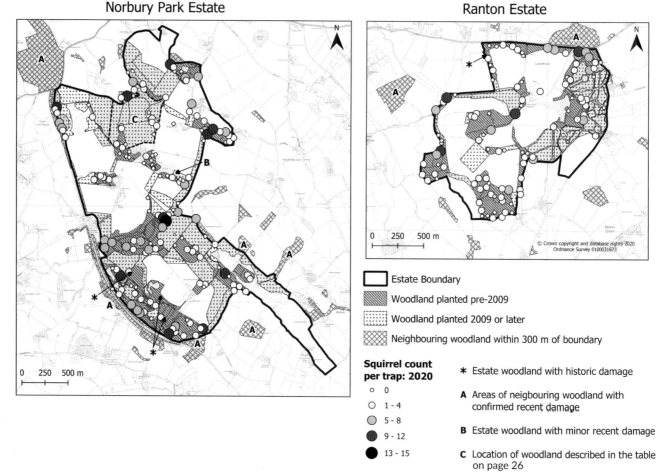

FIGURE 4. *Trap locations with the numbers of squirrels caught per trap in 2020.*

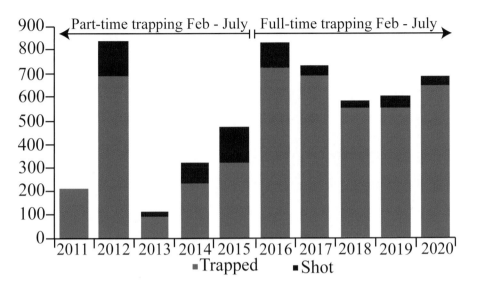

◀

FIGURE 5.

Number of squirrels culled per year.

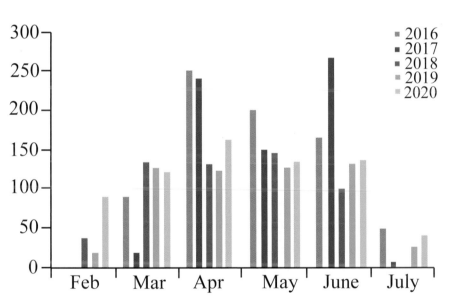

◀

FIGURE 6.

Number of squirrels trapped by month.

squirrels killed per year, many of them pregnant females.

Dead squirrels were initially disposed of via pet shops and butchers. However, because of the large numbers, they were subsequently placed on hedgerows as carrion for crows and buzzards; 50% are taken within a day and all within four days. Our policy has increased the number of buzzards two- to threefold across the estate and they can occasionally be seen catching live squirrels in open areas.

After 11 years of this strategy, we have entirely prevented tree damage except to ten nine-year-old vigorous oak trees during a few days in June 2018 following the removal of traps two weeks earlier (B in figure 4 and

Figure 7). We responded promptly by relocating several traps to platforms in the area, together with shooting.

With our intense targeting of squirrels, damage to oak woodlands in the 20- to 40-year-old age range has been completely eliminated, allowing good recovery from earlier damage. There is now potential for reasonable timber crops. This success contrasts with continuing squirrel damage in neighbouring woodlands on the edges of Norbury Park (Figure 4).

The main cost of squirrel control is a full-time salary for one person for the six months of February through July. The combination of low trapping efficiency and lack of bark damage between August and January means little expense for six months of the year. Other significant costs were 112 Kania 2000 traps at £75.60 each and a small all-terrain vehicle, bringing the recent expenditure to £16,400 per year – perhaps £100,000 over 10 years. Over the 312 ha, this equates to £52 per hectare per year and £24 per squirrel. This compares with £7.90–12.70 per hectare per year in Plashett Wood,[8] £25.50–27 per hectare per year on Bron Haul Farm[9] and nearly £58 per hectare per year at Sotterley Estate (175 ha), where trapping is carried out all year round.[10]

These figures need to be seen in the context of our new woodland costs. We have planted and restocked 180 ha between 2009 and 2020 at a cost of £1.83 million, of which £730,000 was received in grant support from

▲ **FIGURE 7.** *Nine-year-old oak trees recovering from bark stripping damage in 2018.*

the Forestry Commission. We spent £650,000 on trees, guards and stakes, as well as £1.16 million on salaries for planting and subsequent maintenance over the past 11 years, with the balance on incidentals such as vehicles, maintenance, fuel and spraying. Squirrel control costs have been around 5% of the total.

Furthermore, the costs of damage to one hectare of high-quality oak can exceed £45,000.[4] Relative to the final value of an undamaged crop, squirrel control costs are relatively low and may be a good investment in the long term.

During the trapping season, monitoring and setting traps in 314 ha of woodlands is a full-time job. This workload could be reduced if multi-kill Goodnature A18 traps could be utilised effectively, thereby

avoiding daily inspections. But in our experience, they are less efficient and occasionally kill small birds. An alternative would be the introduction of pine martens (Figure 8), which kill grey but not red squirrels.

Squirrel trapping will be a continuing effort for many years – perhaps until the young woodlands are 40 years old, or even older if

▲ **FIGURE 8.** *Pine marten.*

> ## "
> **Squirrel control measures should be compulsory in new plantations, preferably with grant support from the Forestry Commission.**
> "

we wish to prevent damage to tree branches. Furthermore, as trees become larger and grow more vigorously, there will be larger seed crops, leading to lower squirrel mortality during winter and higher reproduction rates.[6] These factors will keep us busy controlling grey squirrels for the foreseeable future* as we remain intent on protecting our beautiful new Staffordshire woodlands.

As others have noted, squirrel control measures should be compulsory in new plantations, preferably with grant support from the Forestry Commission.

*Our approach is in line with current recommendations from Forest Research[11] and *The Grey Squirrel Management Handbook.*[3]

Deer

Fortunately, at present, there are not many deer in the Norbury area so we have had no significant damage. Those few that trespass move quickly through as they are readily disturbed by high woodland activity on the estate or are expertly culled from deer hides (Chapter 2, Figure 2 and Figures 9 and 10).

Deer control is essential. They cause massive damage to UK woodlands by preventing the regrowth of young trees. In highland areas, the only method of stopping complete destruction of young plantations is to erect high fences at a cost of around £28 per metre. There are millions of deer across the country; they have a high reproduction rate and no predators. Culling is the only form of control but there are not enough hunters to make much difference.

▲ **FIGURE 9.** *Deer hide.*

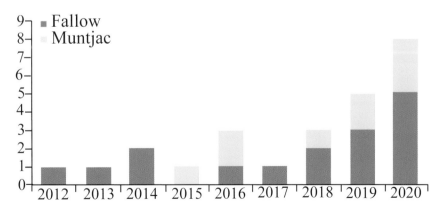

▲ **FIGURE 10.** *Deer culls per year.*

Other animal pests

We have had no problems with rabbits or hares and only one minor issue with voles. In 2014, they ate the roots of over 100 saplings in one small area. They nested inside the bases of tree guards, feasting on the stems and roots of young trees. Removing the tree guards and putting up two raptor perches soon saw them off.

Tree diseases

Inevitably we have been struck by some of the tree diseases rampaging though England. These include ash dieback, acute oak decline and horse chestnut canker. Overall, however, the mixed woodlands have been remarkably disease-free. We have had no fungal disease of larch (*Phytophthora ramorum*), no red band needle blight of pine (*Dothistroma septosporum*) and no spruce bark beetle (*Dendroctonus micans*). Gypsy moth and lackey moth caterpillars, powdery mildew and gall wasps have caused minor damage to oak trees, while woolly aphids (Adelges cooleyi) have affected Douglas fir (Chapter 3). But the only real damage has been inflicted by ash dieback and acute oak decline.

FIGURE 11. *Ash dieback.* ▷

Ash dieback

In the first two years of afforestation (2010 and 2011), when we planted 100,000 trees, 20,000 were ash (Chapter 2, Table 1). That was the advice of our woodland consultants. The popular press was full of reports of ash dieback – infection with *Hymenoscyphus fraxineus*, a fungus imported from Asia – but we were reassured that it would not be a problem. How wrong they were! By the third year of planting (2013), the movement of ash saplings was banned. The ash tree scourge was upon us. I saw it first-hand on a visit to a Suffolk wood: black and dying leaves (Figure 11), drooping young trees with bare stems and mature trees with dead branches.

What would be the fate of our young trees as the fungal infection spread across the country? Within three years we were hit. From no disease in the spring of 2016, it was visible at multiple sites by the autumn. Particularly hard hit were 25-year-old pure ash plantations. They were all infected, with many trees quickly dying.

The young ash trees in the mixed plantations fared rather better. They comprised around 10% of the total, so many were hidden among other tree species. Unexpectedly, some were completely unaffected. As the years pass, more are being infected but many continue to thrive. Despite the scaremongering in the press, we now realise that a good proportion of the trees have considerable disease immunity. One genetic study suggested that up to 30% have modest resistance with 5% being strongly resistant.[12]

This knowledge has become the basis of our strategy. We remove infected trees on an annual basis and paint the stumps with glyphosate to prevent regrowth. In total, we have removed 15,000 trees. While remaining ash trees continue to grow well, further infection is likely. Nevertheless, we anticipate that perhaps 5% will be sufficiently disease-resistant to survive to maturity.

Acute oak decline and sudden oak death

Of our 3,000 mature oak trees, around 50 have died suddenly. One year they are covered in leaves and the next year they are dead. For many of the trees there seems to be no cause, although a few have bleeding cankers (Figure 12), a typical feature of acute oak decline.

Why this is occurring is unclear. There is evidence of fungal invasion, bacterial attack and infestation with oak splendour beetle, but climate warming and waterlogged soils are thought to be additional aggravating factors.

There is no treatment so we remove the infected trees and feed them to the sawmill for beams and planks. Hopefully, these oak diseases will be less of a problem in mixed woodlands. But since the trees are not affected until at least 50 years of age, we have a long wait until we know for sure.

FIGURE 12.

Acute oak decline showing bleeding cankers.

FIGURE 13.

Dutch elm disease in a 'disease-resistant' tree.

Dutch elm disease

The estate includes only a few elm trees. However, we did plant a couple of hundred 10-year-old supposedly disease-resistant trees in the Diamond Wood (Chapter 2). Of the three cultivars, one strain soon succumbed to the disease and these trees were removed (Figure 13). Thankfully, nine years after planting, the other two cultivars remain healthy.

Conclusion

While we cannot be complacent, our huge range of tree species should continue to provide robust protection against serious infections. Active control of pests, particularly grey squirrels and to a lesser extent deer, will safeguard the transition of our new plantations to maturity.

Chapter 7

Birmingham Institute of Forest Research (BIFoR)

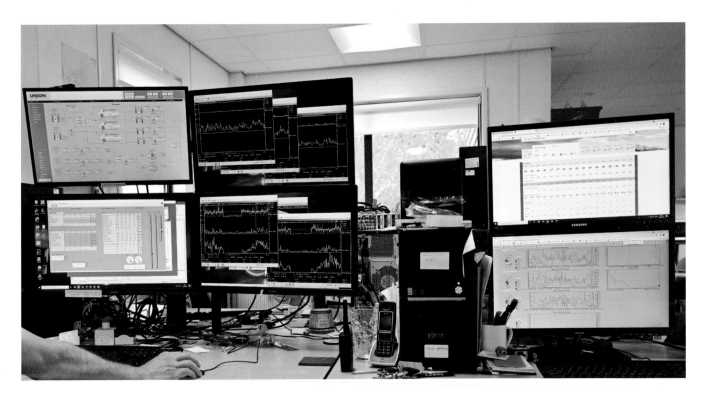

The FACE experiment – the ecological equivalent of the Large Hadron Collider

Looking after a quarter of a million trees is no easy task. This was approximately the number that we acquired when we bought Norbury Park in 2009. When we first visited, I only saw the large oak, beech and larch trees in the broad mature woods with their beautiful summer colours.

> " **All our research points to the fact that forestry can make a significant and cost-effective contribution to meeting the UK's challenging CO$_2$ emissions reduction targets** "
>
> – Sir David Read FRS[1]

I was enchanted by so much nature that I failed to see the dying trees, or those that were damaged by squirrels or were suppressed from years of neglect. It was like buying a house having fallen for the décor and the kitchen Aga while overlooking the ancient plumbing, the out-of-date wiring and the rotten roof timbers. I saw no problems on the estate, only opportunities such as unlimited firewood and beautiful views to the Shropshire hills. But reality soon arrived in the form of squirrels and tree diseases.

FIGURE 1.

Birmingham Institute of Forest Research in Mill Haft at Norbury Park.

I have described how we dealt with pests and diseases in Chapter 6 but this experience set us thinking about the wider picture of woodland management. Compared with other European countries, England has a small forested area – 10% of land area, compared with 37% in France and 32% in Germany. It also has a relatively modest academic forestry sector; for instance, the University at Birmingham, where I had worked most of my life, had no forestry department. As stories of ash dieback, sudden oak death and fungal disease of larch circulated in the popular press, I wondered if the UK's scientific capabilities in such areas were adequate. UK establishments such as Forest Research (the research arm of the Forestry Commission) might be able to mount only a limited response because their funding had been cut repeatedly over the years. We thought that perhaps the sector could benefit from a fresh approach. Professor Sir David Read FRS, Emeritus Professor of Plant Sciences at the University of Sheffield, had overseen the publication of a superb report on how

▲ **FIGURE 2.** *The Synthesis Report.*

more trees were needed to mitigate our CO_2 production and what research should be carried out (Figure 2):

"All our research points to the fact that forestry can make a significant and cost-effective contribution to meeting the UK's challenging CO_2 emissions reduction targets."[1]

I became hooked on his proposals and resolved to found an academic institute of forest research.

To make a difference, a large donation would be needed, preferably to a university with an established track record in forestry. We had a figure of £15 million in mind. Although I had not thought of my alma mater, the University of Birmingham, as a suitable recipient, I thought it would only be polite to approach them first. To our surprise, the Vice-Chancellor,

Sir David Eastwood, welcomed the idea with such enthusiasm that within days we had agreed on a partnership with the University. Professor Malcolm Press, a biologist and a Pro-Vice-Chancellor, was equally enthusiastic.

Together, we agreed that a forestry research programme should address tree diseases, but it should also host an innovative and eye-catching project. By chance, the science journal *Nature* had a front cover describing a tree project proposal for the Amazon rainforest – a 'FACE' (Free Air Carbon Dioxide Enrichment) experiment.[2] The concept was to build a series of tower rings around trees near Manaus in Brazil and enrich the surrounding air with CO_2 to mimic the higher levels predicted 30 years into the future (Figure 3). The aim was to determine whether high atmospheric CO_2 concentrations would be beneficial or harmful to tree growth.

To put this research into context, it is essential to understand the role of forests in mitigating increases in CO_2 concentrations. Rising levels of this greenhouse gas are increasing temperatures world-wide. This is causing, among other things, rises in sea level, more forest fires and progressive damage to marine corals.

It is thought that around one-third of CO_2 emissions from fossil fuels are being absorbed by trees but many uncertainties remain. Forests are complex ecosystems that both absorb and generate CO_2 and other greenhouse gases. It is not yet clear how they might respond to rising CO_2 levels and climate change, but this

could have major implications for the future climate and the role that trees might play in mitigation of climate change.

Behind the FACE concept are numerous scientific experiments and some commercial applications. For instance, it is well known that high levels of CO_2 increase plant growth rates. Indeed, supermarket tomatoes are produced in greenhouses with high levels of CO_2 so that they grow faster. However, experiments in the open air are less common, particularly around large trees in a natural setting. While it is widely accepted that trees grow faster in a higher CO_2 environment, the fear is that this might only be in the short

▲ **FIGURE 3.**

FACE infrastructure in the Amazon.

term. If tree-damaging aphids, for example, ate more leaves as a result of faster tree growth, or diseases became widespread, there might be no increase in carbon sequestration. Furthermore, faster growing trees might run out of essential nutrients such as nitrogen and phosphorus, which would limit size increases. There have been some FACE experiments in planted woodlands, including one at Bangor University in North Wales, but few studies have explored the potential long-term effects of higher CO_2 levels on natural woodland. One exception is an early-stage FACE experiment among eucalyptus trees near Sydney, Australia. However, since such woodlands are uncommon elsewhere, results from these studies might be difficult to extrapolate to other parts of the world. By contrast, temperate woodlands in the UK are representative of about 30% of the world's forests. Results will therefore be much more relevant to policymaking on climate change.

This became our signature experiment – a huge FACE project that would animate the forestry sector and bring tree, plant and soil scientists to Birmingham. The media have even termed it the ecological equivalent of the Large Hadron Collider at CERN.

In 2013, as plans were developed by the University under the watchful eye of the project director, Professor Rob MacKenzie, we agreed to lease to the University a 10-hectare flat area of mature oak woodland at Norbury Park called Mill Haft (Chapter 1, Figure 1). Within

the woodland there would be constructed six tower rings, each of which would surround six to eight mature oak trees and their understories of coppiced hazel and the occasional ash and sycamore. Into these rings would be pumped CO_2 at levels expected in 30 years' time – an extra 150 parts per million (ppm) above ambient concentrations (Figure 4).

The requirements were prodigious: six tower rings, three with CO_2 enrichment and three identical control rings blowing air, plus three 'ghost' rings as controls for the effects of the huge infrastructures. The active tower rings release 20 tonnes of CO_2 per day. Because of the huge cost of the CO_2 (£100 per tonne), it was quickly agreed that enrichment would be restricted to daytime and when the trees were in leaf (April through October). These are the periods of active photosynthesis (when leaves use light energy to convert water and CO_2 into carbohydrate/sugar).

Each of the tower rings comprises 30 metal fabrications that stretch to above the tree canopy (around 30 metres). Attached to the towers are a manifold of CO_2 delivery tubes, while sensors positioned throughout

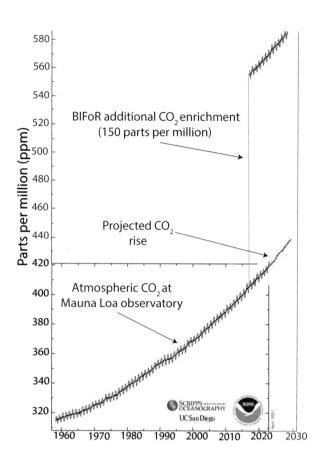

△ **FIGURE 4.**

Rising atmospheric CO_2 levels since 1960 and BIFoR enrichment with an additional 150ppm.

the centre of the rings regulate the computer-controlled release of CO_2 on a second-by-second basis. All these components had to be constructed with minimal damage to the woodland and certainly with no concrete emplacements. Ably fabricated by Shaylor Construction Ltd (which won a design award for its efforts), the stainless-steel tower bases were screwed into the soil while the towers were lifted into place by

▲ **FIGURE 5.**

Placing CO$_2$ enrichment towers through Mill Haft tree canopy.

a helicopter that threaded each one down through the woodland canopy.

The latter operation proved to be particularly challenging as the downdraft from the rotor blades violently shook the treetops and broke some branches. Over 10 days, only a few of the 120 towers were lowered into position. The solution was a special double-rotor helicopter flown in from Switzerland. With its blades at an angle to the ground, the downdraft was not directly below the helicopter so the tree canopy remained stable. Remarkably, within a day and a half, all the rings were complete (Figures 5 to 7).

▲ **FIGURE 6.**

CO$_2$ enrichment towers surrounding mature oak trees.

▶ **FIGURE 7.**

The six FACE rings and the central monitoring tower in Mill Haft wood.

Additional infrastructure items were the three CO_2 storage tanks holding 40 tonnes of CO_2 under high pressure (Figure 8), heat exchangers to bring the gas to ambient temperatures and a kilometre of ducting (Figure 9). Experts from Brookhaven in the USA and Sydney in Australia were brought in to oversee the construction.

By early 2016, the construction was complete which allowed one year for the collection of baseline data before CO_2 enrichment commenced in 2017. Kris Hart was appointed as operations manager with Nick Harper as senior engineer.

Constructing the facility had been quite a challenge, but accurately controlling CO_2 levels throughout the arrays proved just as difficult. Wind across the woods varies continuously in terms of speed and direction and from ground level to the canopy top. In strong winds, it is impossible to control CO_2 concentrations so enrichment is stopped. Even with mild winds,

▲ **FIGURE 8.** *CO_2 storage containers.*

the valves on the downwind side of the arrays are switched off, as any released gas immediately drifts into the surrounding woods. Nevertheless, despite these difficulties, elevated CO_2 concentrations have been remarkably well maintained (Figures 10 to 12).[3]

Although BIFoR's CO_2 usage is prodigious – 20 to 25 tonnes per day, equivalent to 2.5% of the UK supply – it rapidly mixes with the surrounding air. (The CO_2 is a by-product of fertiliser manufacturing and would normally be released into the atmosphere anyway.) Adding CO_2 at 150 ppm in a free-air situation is not a human health risk – CO_2 levels can reach 2,000–3,000 ppm in unventilated bedrooms or stuffy

▲ **FIGURE 9.** *Tower bases with CO_2 ducting.*

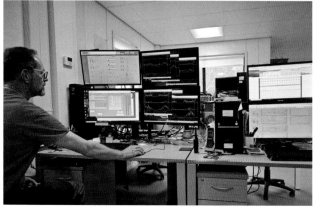

▲ **FIGURE 10.** *Nick Harper monitoring CO_2 enrichment in the arrays.*

meeting rooms. The CO_2 released in this experiment is a tiny increase in the local atmosphere and is quickly dissipated.

With all the equipment in place by 2017, the experiments could begin. A few of the important ones are indicated below, while a fuller list is provided in Appendix 10 and on the BIFoR website: www.birmingham.ac.uk/research/bifor/face.aspx.

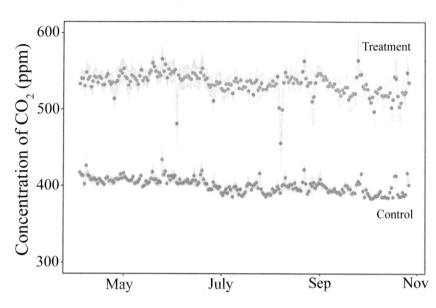

FIGURE 11. *Ambient and enriched CO_2 concentrations in two arrays over eight months.*

▼ **FIGURE 12.**

Arborist checking the canopy and FACE towers.

Above ground:

Measuring tree stem growth (Figure 13), sampling leaves, buds and catkins, leaf area measurements and leaf litter traps (Figure 14) and quantifying methane fluxes from tree trunks (Figure 15).

Below ground vegetation:

Assessing fine root development (Figure 16), soil CO_2 (Figure 17), water fluxes, nitrogen mineralisation, pH, soil type and organic matter content.

FIGURE 13.

PhD student Laura Brammeld measuring tree diameter and sap flow.

FIGURE 14.

Collecting leaf litter.

FIGURE 15.

Site of methane flux measurements on an oak trunk.

Atmospheric processes:

Measuring wind speed, CO_2 concentrations, water and methane fluxes, solar and net radiation, air temperature, and relative humidity profile.

Animals:

Monitoring mammal activity through camera traps installed in the woodland.

▲ **FIGURE 16.** *Rhizotron tube for observing roots.*

▲ **FIGURE 17.** *Measuring soil respiration (CO_2, N_2 and O_2).*

Early results

The central question for the BIFoR FACE experiment is: do higher CO_2 concentrations increase tree growth in the short, medium and long term? In the short term the answer is yes. After five years of enrichment, which is short term in a tree's life, oak growth is 10–15% higher within the CO_2 enrichment rings than in the control rings. Furthermore, there is a 20% increase in root growth, suggesting that the trees are seeking more nutrients deep within the soil. By contrast, there is no increase in leaf area, although photosynthesis rates are 30% higher (similar to the increase in CO_2 concentrations).[4]

These results are good news because they indicate that the trees are absorbing more CO_2 and growing faster. However, whether increased growth rates will continue in the medium term is unknown. Results from the FACE facility in Australia suggest that essential nutrients such as nitrogen and phosphorous may be limiting factors. If so, it may be important to plant nitrogen-fixing tree species in our future woodlands (Chapter 2). With funding in place for seven more years, BIFoR is in an excellent position to find out.

Since construction, the facility has become widely known, with visits from Lord Gardiner of Kimble (formerly Parliamentary Under Secretary of State for Rural Affairs and Biosecurity at the Department for the Environment, Food and Rural Affairs – DEFRA), Professor Sir Mark Walport (formerly Government Chief Scientific Adviser), Professor Sir Ian Boyd (formerly Chief Scientific Officer at DEFRA), and many other scientists from the UK and abroad. In July 2018, It was a great pleasure to be visited by HRH Charles, Prince of Wales. After preliminary enquiries from Staffordshire police, the Royal Household and Her Majesty's Lord-Lieutenant of Staffordshire, Ian Dudson, HRH flew in by helicopter and spent a few hours with us talking to professors and students alike (Figure 18).

When the experiments are complete, all the infrastructure will be removed and the woodland will be returned to its original condition.

▲ **FIGURE 18.**

The author and Prince Charles visiting the BIFoR FACE facility in July 2018.

BIFoR and tree diseases

The other main aim of BIFoR is to investigate tree diseases and tree pathology. Professor Rob Jackson, a recent appointment to the board of BIFoR noted:

"Ash dieback was first reported in Poland in 1992 and by the time it was reported in Britain in 2012, the death rate among young ash trees was up to 80% with tens of millions dead across Europe. It became a national emergency leading to Governmental COBR meetings. ('COBR' is an acronym for 'Cabinet Office Briefing Rooms', where committees meet to coordinate the response to national crises.) The meetings highlighted poor biosecurity, lack of tree disease monitoring and the realisation there was no ability to treat infections or immunise the healthy: quite a parallel with COBR meetings on COVID-19 in early 2020. For the 125 million ash trees in the UK, it means well over 100 million deaths at an estimated removal cost of £15 billion. How similar is this to Dutch elm disease of the 1960s, which killed 90% of our English elm trees, over 20 million in total?"

While the fungal disease of ash dieback is being closely studied, there is very little analysis of tree diseases caused by bacteria in the UK. Trees in the UK and Europe suffering from bacterial infections typically have features in the trunk and limbs in the form of effusive bleeds (cankers) and staining of the wood. Bacterial diseases of trees can be roughly divided into two groups based on the specific bacteria involved: walnut, willow, poplar, alder and oak can be infected by a range of bacterial pathogens, including *Erwinia*, *Brenneria*, *Gibbsiella*, *Rahnella and Lonsdalea*; by contrast, horse chestnut, cherry and ash all suffer infections with *Pseudomonas* bacteria.

Many questions remain unanswered, including how bacteria get into trees, how they cause disease and tree death, how they spread to other trees, and how they can be treated. Numerous projects investigating these questions are underway on the University of Birmingham campus in Edgbaston and at Norbury Park.

Conclusion

BIFoR is of national and international significance. Substantial funding has been obtained from our JABBS Foundation (£22m), the Natural Environment Research Council (£4.2m), the Leverhulme Trust (£1m), the Wolfson Trust (£1m), the John Horseman Trust (£300,000), the Royal Society (£240,000) plus many other smaller donations and grants, together with financial support from the University of Birmingham.

Recently, and after many years of discussions, the FACE facility in the Amazon may finally receive funding from the German and UK Governments. There are also plans to construct a FACE facility in the great boreal forests of the north so that the responses to rising CO_2 are understood in all three major forest types around the world – tropical, temperate and boreal. Only then can climate change scientists accurately model CO_2 fluxes on land.

▼ **FIGURE 19.** *BIFoR FACE facility management team. Lt to rt: Peter Miles, Kris Hart, Nick Harper and Thomas Downes.*

Chapter 8

Carbon sequestration at Norbury Park

Old growth Coast redwoods in California storing 4,300 tonnes of carbon per hectare – the highest tree storage of carbon in the world.

Doley Brook leading to Doley Common a SSSI at Norbury Park
containing deep peat in wetlands with huge carbon stores.

"You must unite behind the science. You must take action." Greta Thunberg – US Congress, Washington DC, 17 September 2019

Norbury Park is sequestering large amounts of carbon in its woodlands and into soils under the herbal leys. Back-of-an-envelope calculations suggested 3,000 to 4,000 tonnes annually (based on a few tree sizes and soil carbon measurements) but we wanted more accurate numbers, not only to be more confident of what we were achieving but also to make further improvements where possible.

With this aim in mind, we engaged Becky Wilson's consultancy firm, which uses the proprietary Farm Carbon Toolkit to assess carbon balance on agricultural properties. In simplistic terms, it involves filling out a large spreadsheet covering every component of an estate where carbon is involved. These range from obvious factors such as the amount of diesel fuel used in vehicles and woodland growth, to obscure issues such as embedded carbon in concrete, livestock emissions and tyre wear.

After several weeks of detailed data collection, the figures for 2020 showed that the growing woodlands and the arable soils sequestered 2,959 tonnes and 3,011 tonnes respectively, and solar PV offset 18 tonnes, while we emitted 711 tonnes of CO_2 from farm, woodland and other management activities. These components resulted in a final balance of 5,277 tonnes in credit (Figure 1), more than 50% above our original estimations. This is because of enhanced tree growth rates and good increases in soil carbon concentrations. However, repeat measurements are needed to be certain of the long-term effects of our woodland and farmland policies.

Further analyses of the components are shown in the following pie charts. Figures 2-5 show the origin of CO_2 emissions at Norbury Park, while the last pie chart (Figure 6) shows CO_2 sequestration into different species of trees.

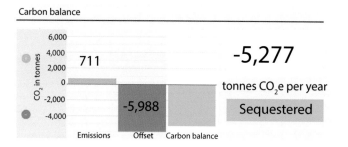

◀ **FIGURE 1.**
Overall CO_2 balance in 2020.

Carbon emissions – the negative side of the equation

1. CO_2 emissions from fuels – 350 tonnes (49% of total emissions).

This is dominated by the use of woodchip derived from tree thinning of young and old woodland (Figure 2).

2. Emissions from materials – 3 tonnes (0.4% of total emissions).

These relate to items such as fence posts, packaging, office materials and tyre use; the total is trivial and not considered further.

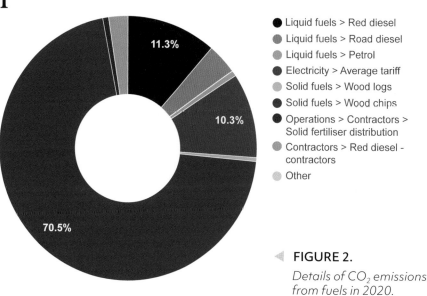

◀ **FIGURE 2.**
Details of CO_2 emissions from fuels in 2020.

3. Emissions from inventory – 111 tonnes (15.6% of total emissions).

This is the embedded CO_2 that is emitted during the production of machinery and construction of buildings (Figure 3). One tenth of the emissions associated with manufacture are attributed to the footprint for each of the first ten years, after which the item has paid its carbon debt. The substantial number of refurbishment and building projects across the estate have contributed to these emissions. However, the figures are relatively low compared with CO_2 emissions during normal refurbishments because of the widespread use of estate-grown timber. The additional carbon cost using external materials would have been around 80 tonnes of CO_2.

4. Emissions associated with crops – 28 tonnes (3.9% of total emissions).

This is dominated by the use of lime but also includes a small amount from crop residue breakdown (Figure 4).

5. Emissions for fertiliser use, herbicides and fungicides – 71 tonnes (10% of total emissions).

Our fertiliser use on farmland is low compared with other estates. We apply a variety of blended products to the land, which contributes just under 75% of total emissions in this category Figure 4). A total of 30 tonnes of nitrogen fertiliser were used in 2020; this amount will reduce as we convert all herbal leys from silage production to mob grazing with cattle (Chapter 5).

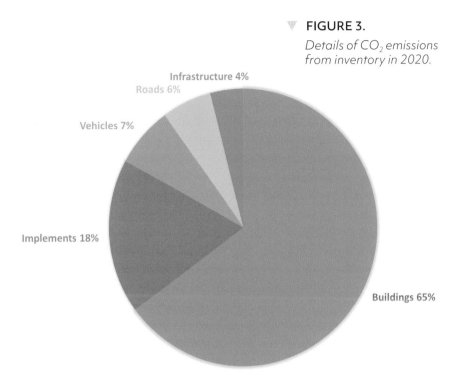

FIGURE 3.
Details of CO_2 emissions from inventory in 2020.

Infrastructure 4% · Roads 6% · Vehicles 7% · Implements 18% · Buildings 65%

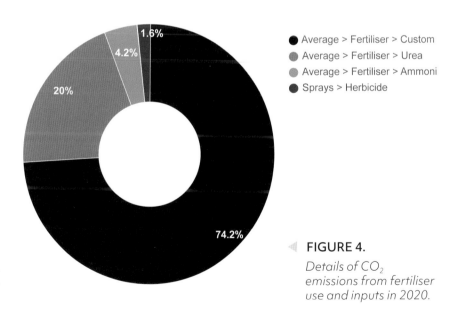

● Average > Fertiliser > Custom
● Average > Fertiliser > Urea
● Average > Fertiliser > Ammoni
● Sprays > Herbicide

1.6% · 4.2% · 20% · 74.2%

FIGURE 4.
Details of CO_2 emissions from fertiliser use and inputs in 2020.

> " Woodland CO$_2$ sequestration is high because of the large land area – 314 hectares – and the innovative practice of halo-pollarding young trees. "

▷

FIGURE 5.

Details of CO$_2$ emissions from livestock in 2020.

6. Emissions from livestock – 108 tonnes (15% of total emissions).

The emissions within this category are solely from livestock that are brought in from neighbouring farms to graze the herbal leys (Figure 5).

7. Emissions from waste – 0.38 tonnes (0.05% of total emissions).

Emissions are trivial and will not be considered further.

8. Emissions from distribution – 40 tonnes (5.6% of total emissions).

These emissions relate to timber lorries; totals are calculated by taking account of the number of journeys, the distance travelled and the loads carried. As Shelmore Timber is selling wood products, the haulage CO$_2$ footprint is included. It is common farming practice to exclude this category in carbon emission calculations, possibly to make footprints look better.

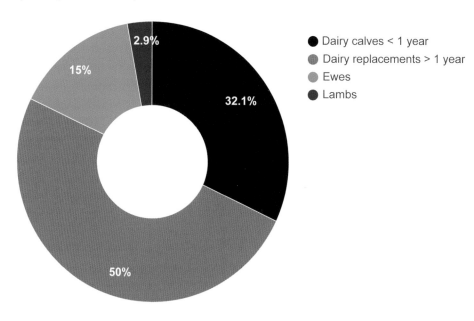

- ● Dairy calves < 1 year
- ◐ Dairy replacements > 1 year
- ● Ewes
- ● Lambs

The figures from these eight categories add up to the rounded total of 711 tonnes of CO$_2$ emissions as shown in Figure 1 and Figure 7.

Carbon sequestration and offsets – the positive side of the equation

Carbon is sequestered in two ways: in woodland habitats and in soils beneath the herbal leys. Minor additional carbon offsets are obtained from solar PV arrays and recycling.

1. Sequestration in woodland, hedgerows and habitats – 2,959 tonnes (49.4% of total).

For the woodlands, total sequestration is calculated by measuring a representative sample of the growth of the trees and adding 25% for the growth of tree roots (Figure 6). Woodland CO_2 sequestration is high because of the large land area – 314 hectares – and the innovative practice of halo-pollarding young trees (Chapter 2). This has increased growth rates in the young plantations by at least 30%, adding significantly to CO_2 sequestration.

The estate includes 18 km of hedgerows, of which 13 km are flailed annually (sequestering 17 tonnes of CO_2) and nearly 5 km that are left to grow (sequestering 24 tonnes of CO_2). If none of the hedges were cut annually, an additional 44 tonnes of CO_2 would be absorbed per year. Woodland margins and glades are contributing 46 tonnes and the cattle-grazed, Site of Special Scientific Interest that contains deep peat (Chapter 1, Figure 1), together with ponds/lakes, are providing 59 tonnes of CO_2 uptake.

FIGURE 6. ▼

Details of CO_2 sequestration in woodlands and similar habitats in 2020.

2. Soil carbon sequestration as soil organic matter in herbal leys – 3,011 tonnes (50.3% of total).

In the herbal leys, soil organic matter was measured to a depth of 50 cm on multiple sites across the estate in 2021 and compared with measurements five years earlier. Over this period, soil organic matter has increased from 2.5% to 3.5%. This increase of 1% over five years (0.2% per year) on 194 hectares corresponds to an increase in sequestered CO_2 in 2020 of 3,011 tonnes. More accurate soil sampling in a few years will improve the accuracy of the carbon sequestration calculation.

3. Offsets comprising 100 mW of solar PV and recycling – 18 tonnes (0.3% of total).

The rather expensive solar panels (Chapter 4) and recycling only contributed a small amount to our total carbon sequestration/offset.

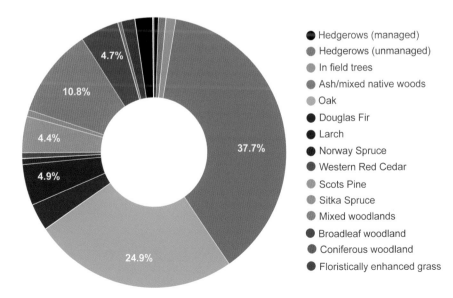

- ● Hedgerows (managed)
- ● Hedgerows (unmanaged)
- ● In field trees
- ● Ash/mixed native woods
- ● Oak
- ● Douglas Fir
- ● Larch
- ● Norway Spruce
- ● Western Red Cedar
- ● Scots Pine
- ● Sitka Spruce
- ● Mixed woodlands
- ● Broadleaf woodland
- ● Coniferous woodland
- ● Floristically enhanced grass

Summary chart of CO_2 balance at Norbury Park in 2020

Figure 7 is a graphical representation (on a log scale) of CO_2 emitted at Norbury Park (red) and sequestration (green) with the balance of 5,277 tonnes in dark green.

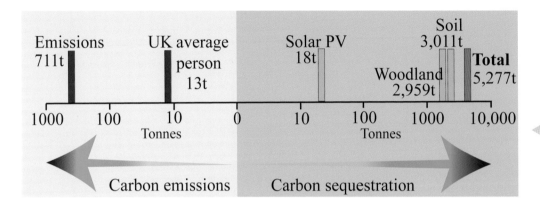

◀ **FIGURE 7.**

Norbury Park CO_2 emissions, sequestration and offsets in 2020 (log scale).

Comparison with other farms and estates in 2020

At Norbury we have made a determined effort to sequester as much carbon as possible. This has involved huge investments in woodlands and a complete change from arable crops to herbal leys with mob grazing. The outcome has been dramatic in terms of annual CO_2 sequestration per hectare and compares very favourably with nine other representative farms and estates where we had access to their carbon balance figures (Figure 8 – on a log scale). Our exceptional carbon sequestration cannot be achieved without a high percentage of woodland cover, innovative silviculture and the increase in soil carbon from a low base after intense arable farming.

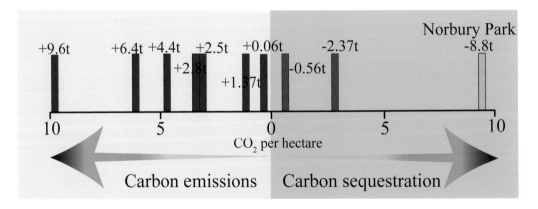

▲ **FIGURE 8.**

Norbury Park CO_2 sequestration per hectare in 2020 compared with nine other farms and estates (log scale).

Future prospects

As 2020 is the first year in which we have calculated the CO_2 balance at Norbury Park, it is still a work in progress. We need to make repeated measurements of soil organic carbon to improve the accuracy of the calculations, as well as longer-term measurements of growth patterns in the young woodlands.

One improvement in carbon offset under consideration is an increase in solar PV arrays from 100 kW to 235 kW. Although expensive (Chapter 4), this should add an extra 50 tonnes of CO_2 offset per year. Another scheme is to add ground-granulated blast-furnace slag (known as GGBS) to the concrete floor of a new fire log drying shed, which will reduce the carbon footprint of construction by 29 tonnes.

Importantly, as the young woodlands approach maturity over future decades, their growth rates will accelerate, increasing CO_2 sequestration at Norbury Park. In addition, the widespread use of mob grazing with cattle should maintain a steady increase in soil carbon sequestration. We anticipate that our positive annual carbon balance will increase beyond the 5,277 tonnes that were sequestered in 2020.

Chapter 9
Afforestation – politics, policies and people

▼   Logging the Amazon.

Tree lovers rejoice – the woods are coming back

With the stroke of a pen in his 1988 budget, Chancellor Nigel Lawson removed tax relief on forestry expenditure and with it, 70 years of continuity for this vital rural enterprise. Tree planting plummeted from over 30,000 hectares per year to an eventual low of 5,400 hectares in 2010. This was despite inheritance tax relief on commercially managed forestry, together with woodland creation grants from the Forestry Commission.

The tax relief removal was due to the public fuss over the planting of conifer monocultures in the Flow Country of Sutherland (Figure 1), which seemed to benefit only the rich.

But the unintended consequence of the law change was a drastic curtailment of tree planting in the UK from which it has never recovered. Since 1988, opportunities for robust forest creation have been lost. Only now is there a resurgence of interest. The reason – a looming climate change disaster that can be partly mitigated by planting trees to absorb CO_2.

◁ **FIGURE 1.**
Flow Country conifer forests.

The 2016 Paris Agreement

In 2016, the UK Government signed up to the Paris Agreement on Climate Change, whose key aim is:

> *"To hold the increase in the global average temperature to well below 2°C above pre-industrial levels and to pursue efforts to limit the temperature increase to 1.5°C above pre-industrial levels, recognizing that this would significantly reduce the risks and impacts of climate change."*

Unfortunately, the agreement is not going according to plan. An article in *Nature* found that, as of 2017, none of the major industrialised nations were implementing the policies they had pledged to introduce, and none had met their pledged emission reduction targets.[1] Even if they had, the sum of all member pledges (as of 2016) would still not keep the global temperature rise 'well below 2°C'.[2] According to the 2020 United Nations Environment Programme, even with the current climate commitments of the Paris Agreement, global mean temperatures are likely to rise by more than 3°C by the end of the 21st century.

However, the Paris Agreement has given ammunition to those seeking to achieve change. In May 2021, in a first-of-its-kind case, environmental organisations in The Netherlands brought a case against oil company Royal Dutch Shell. In *Milieudefensie et al v Royal Dutch Shell*, the court decided that the company must cut its global emissions by 45% from 2019 levels by 2030, as it was in violation of the European Convention on Human Rights. This lawsuit was considered the first time the Paris Agreement had been used against a corporation.[3]

The myth that burning wood is carbon neutral

There are other court actions in prospect. One relates to the burning of biofuels, which are classified as carbon neutral under the Kyoto Protocol,[4] so nations do not need to count wood burning for energy production among their Paris Agreement carbon emissions. This has led to the myth that burning logs and wood pellets is carbon neutral. In the UK, Drax power station burns millions of tons of wood pellets from the USA (Figure 2) but the CO_2 produced is just the same as CO_2 produced by fossil fuels. It is a great deception that burning biofuels is better for the environment – **it is not.** CO_2 is sequestered when trees grow and emitted when they are burnt. In our carbon emissions calculations at Norbury Park, we correctly account for our woodchip boilers as producing 250 tonnes of CO_2 emissions in 2020 (Chapter 8, Figure 3).

The acceptability of burning biofuels including woodfuels is now becoming a political issue:

"On Monday, 4 March, 2021, in the European General Court in Luxembourg (Figure 3), plaintiffs in five European nations and the US filed suit against the European Union. At issue is the EU's rapid conversion of coal-burning powerplants to burn wood pellets and chips, a process known as bioenergy. Activists see the EU's bioenergy policies as reckless and endangering the climate," said Mary

▲ **FIGURE 2.** *Drax power station burning wood pellets.*

◀ **FIGURE 3.** *European Court of Justice in Luxembourg.*

S Booth, director of the US-based Partnership for Policy Integrity. She continued, *"The EU's policy on biofuels relies on the false and reckless assumption that burning forest wood is carbon neutral. However, scientists from around the world, including the EU's own science advisers, have warned that burning forest wood actually increases emissions relative to fossil fuels."* This is because they are being transported large distances such as from America to the UK and are being processed into pellets or woodchip, both of which produce CO_2.

The UK Government is making big commitments to climate change

In December 2020, the UK committed to a 68% reduction in climate change emissions by 2030.[5] Four months later, in April 2021, it committed to a 78% reduction in climate emissions by 2035,[6] having already agreed to become carbon neutral by 2050 (Figure 4).

Part of the UK's planned reductions in CO_2 emissions include carbon sequestration in growing forests. In May 2021, this was detailed in The Trees Action Plan 2021–2024.[7]

As announced by the Rt Hon George Eustice MP, Secretary of State for Environment, Food and Rural Affairs: "Trees and woodlands have a vital role in delivering net zero greenhouse gas emissions by 2050, achieving the goals of our 25 Year Environment Plan, and delivering on our ambitions to conserve and enhance biodiversity."

"The Government has committed to increasing tree planting rates across the UK to 30,000 hectares per year by the end of this Parliament. To achieve this, we are intending to spend over £500 million of the £640 million Nature for Climate Fund on trees and woodlands in England between 2020 and 2025 to support this ambition. And by planting the right trees in the right places for the right reasons, we can do so much more than just sequester carbon. This plan aims to see current planting trends for majority native broadleaf woodlands continue, given the additional benefits they provide for nature and people."[7]

There are innumerable components to these ambitious and welcome proposals but they include key policies to promote forestry:

- Supporting land-owners to create new woodlands
- Encouraging the use of timber in construction
- Supporting innovative approaches to forestry
- Adapting trees and woodlands to the impacts of climate change
- Developing deer and grey squirrel management plans nationally.

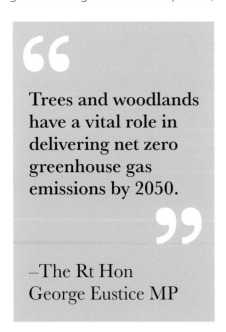

Trees and woodlands have a vital role in delivering net zero greenhouse gas emissions by 2050.

–The Rt Hon George Eustice MP

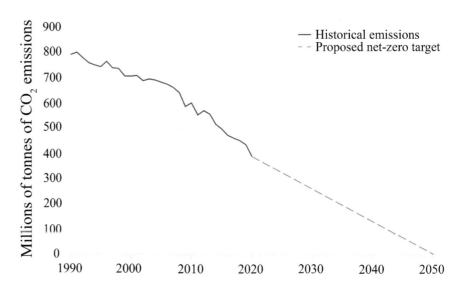

▶ **FIGURE 4.** *50% fall in UK emissions since 1990.*

How much CO$_2$ will be captured if 30,000 hectares of woodland are planted every year for 30 years?

In June 2019, the UK's Climate Change Committee recommended that the UK should plant around 30,000 hectares of new woodland every year from 2020 until 2050[8,9] – in other words, nearly a million hectares. At 10 tonnes of CO$_2$ sequestration per hectare per year, the forests would eventually capture 10 million tonnes per year, although this would require either fast-growing conifers or complex mixtures on good soils. Currently there are 3.1 million hectares of woodland in the UK, which absorb perhaps five to ten tonnes per hectare per year. Total CO$_2$ capture is therefore currently around 20 million tonnes per year. With new planting, the combined total could be 30 million tonnes of CO$_2$ captured per year by 2050. This is not much considering that we are currently emitting 350 million tonnes per year (plus similar amounts of CO$_2$ embedded in products manufactured abroad but used in the UK). However, although 30 million tonnes may not seem a lot at the moment, it would certainly be important for capturing residual CO$_2$ emissions towards 2050. Needless to say, to capture the CO$_2$, we need to plant trees right now since they sequester very little when they are small.

Another myth: planting one giant redwood provides a lifetime of CO$_2$ offset

An article in *The Times* on 21 November 2020 by environment editor Ben Webster was titled, 'Giant sequoias (also called Giant redwoods and Wellingtonia) will take root in Britain'. In it, he claimed, 'each one will offset a person's lifetime emissions'. **This is nonsense.** He continued, 'they capture ten times more than planting native UK trees' – **complete nonsense.**

I planted a Giant sequoia 33 years ago; it is 10 metres high and probably weighs less than one tonne. A 150-year-old tree at Norbury Park weighs maybe 15 tonnes (Figure 5). Currently the largest Giant redwood in the UK is 58 metres tall and, after 170 years, weighs perhaps 20 tonnes. Hardly a lifetime offset when the average annual CO$_2$ emission per person in the UK is 13 tonnes. Simple solutions like individuals sponsoring a Giant redwood aren't going to make much difference!

▷ **FIGURE 5.**
40 m Giant redwood at Norbury Park.

Where might the trees be planted?

The area of woodland in the UK in 2020 was estimated to be 3.1 million hectares. This represents 13% of the total land area of the UK – 10% in England, 15% in Wales, 19% in Scotland and 9% in Northern Ireland. One million additional hectares (a little over 30,000 hectares per year for 30 years) would increase this to 17.2% of the UK land area. This is twice the area of the county of Somerset. Since 84% of the UK population live in England, maybe 84% of the trees should be planted in England – which would be 840,000 hectares. This would be 6.5% of the surface area of England and would increase its woodland cover to 16.5%. This might be particularly relevant if Scotland becomes independent of the UK and retains its own CO_2 sequestration targets.

Where can one million hectares of land be found in the UK? After all, one million extra hectares is only a 30% increase in woodland cover compared with what we currently have. The top 50 landowners currently control nearly three million hectares (Appendix 2). Much of this is highland and peat moors, but by no means all.

There are 3.2 million hectares of National Parks in the UK, of which 1.6 million hectares are in England and Wales (Appendix 3). The differences between woodland cover across individual parks are surprisingly large. The Lake District covers 236,000 hectares and is 12% forested, while the Peak District National Park's 144,000 hectares are only 0.3% forested. Surely, in all those huge areas of National Parks, a decent proportion could be beautified with mixed woodlands?

Other land areas that might be considered are hill-sheep grazing pastures. They used to be woodlands when the UK was 90% forested in Neolithic times, but now provide subsidized incomes for a modest number of farmers. Could some be converted into woodlands with all the benefits of increased biodiversity, public access, job creation and increased carbon sequestration?

TABLE 1.

Top ten landowners in the UK.

Landowner	Hectares
Forestry Commission	890,328
Ministry of Defence	445,913
Crown Estate	274,553
National Trust and National Trust for Scotland	238,668
Royal Society for the Protection of Birds	134,359
Richard Scott, Duke of Buccleuch and Queensberry	113,314
Anders Holch Povlsen	88,371
Duke of Atholl's Trusts	58,681
United Utilities	56,707
Hugh Grosvenor, 7th Duke of Westminster	56,657

How much will new woodlands cost?

At Norbury we planted 180 hectares of new woodlands between 2009 and 2020 at a cost of £1.83 million (Chapter 2). Converted into the UK Government's planting target of 30,000 hectares per year, this would amount to £305 million per year, not accounting for any land costs or inflation. If a land cost of £6,000 per acre were added, this would increase costs by £180 million per year, making the total around £500 million per year or £15 billion over 30 years. Of the £1.83 million we spent on our woodlands at Norbury, 40% (£730,000) came from grant support for tree planting. Currently, the Government has pledged £500 million for woodlands throughout the UK. It won't go far.

An alternative approach would be to decide on a target amount of carbon sequestration. If it were agreed that a total of 25 million tonnes of CO_2 sequestration were needed per year by 2050, then innovative tree planting, with complex mixtures (Figures 6 and 8) and active management of these and older woodlands, would require less land and would be less expensive (Chapter 2). With innovative approaches, land take could perhaps be halved.

FIGURE 6.
Mixed conifer plantation.

What policies need to be in place to get the trees planted?

Government support is essential in terms of grants and active political encouragement. Since we all love trees, policies that promote woodland creation will enjoy huge public sympathy and electoral support. Ten golden rules for woodland creation were recently suggested by Professor Alexandre Antonelli, Director of Science at the Royal Botanic Gardens, Kew, and colleagues[10]:

1. **Protect existing forests first.**
    Keeping forests in their original state is always preferable; undamaged old forests soak up carbon better and are more resilient to fire, storm and droughts. He emphasised that: "Whenever there's a choice, we stress that halting deforestation and protecting remaining forests must be a priority."

2. **Put local people at the heart of tree-planting projects.**
    Studies show that getting local communities on board is key to the success of tree-planting projects. It is often local people who have most to gain from looking after the forest in the future.

3. **Maximise biodiversity recovery to meet multiple goals.**
Reforestation should be about several goals, including guarding against climate change, improving conservation and providing economic and cultural benefits.

4. **Select the right area for reforestation.**
Plant trees in areas that were historically forested but have become degraded, rather than using other natural habitats such as grasslands or wetlands.

5. **Use natural forest regrowth wherever possible.**
Letting trees grow back naturally can be cheaper and more efficient than planting trees. *(Author's note: This may be cheaper but carbon sequestration is much slower with natural regeneration).*

6. **Select the right tree species to maximise biodiversity.**
Where tree planting is needed, picking the right trees is crucial. Scientists advise a mixture of tree species naturally found in the local area, including some rare species and trees of economic importance, but avoiding trees that might become invasive.

7. **Make sure the trees are resilient to a changing climate.**
Use tree seeds that are suitable for the local climate and how it might change in the future.

8. **Plan ahead.**
Plan how to source seeds or trees, working with local people.

9. **Learn by doing.**
Combine scientific knowledge with local knowledge. Ideally, small-scale trials should take place before planting large numbers of trees.

10. **Make it pay.**
The sustainability of tree re-planting rests on a source of income for all stakeholders, including the poorest. Woodlands will provide jobs, jobs and more jobs.

Above all, for tree-planting projects to succeed, local people must be given a place at the heart of them. They are the ones with a stake in their new amenity as the saplings grow. They will also need to defend them from pressure groups such as climate change deniers, rewilders, grey squirrel and deer lovers, private estates with grouse or pheasant shoots and arable and sheep farmers. The list is endless. Large afforestation projects need public acceptance and support to be successful, as suggested above.

▲ **FIGURE 7.** *National tree-planting day in Ethiopia.*

Possibly a myth?

Ethiopia held a one-day tree-planting event on 29 July 2019, with an initial target to plant 200 million saplings across the country (Figure 7). The government announced that the target had been exceeded, with more than 350 million planted over a 12-hour period and four billion trees over three months. The outcome has not been confirmed as a Guinness world record.[11] Nevertheless, what an inspirational effort!

How might Norbury Park tree experiments affect future forestry plantations in the UK?

Experiments in forestry take years to complete so a policy of informed practice based on the best available evidence has to be formulated. The fast growth rates of our mixed plantations are supported by many scientific studies that show complex intimate mixtures grow faster and are less susceptible to pests and diseases. It is time to move away from classical forestry practices of planting woodlands with few tree species and with limited thinning cycles.

We propose the following:

1. Include 20–30 different species in new woodlands in order to improve growth rates, resilience to temperature rises, pests and diseases (Chapter 3).

2. Include species from other countries (Chapter 2).

3. Mix conifers with deciduous trees (Figure 8).

4. Include nitrogen-fixing trees (Chapter 2).

5. Apply active silviculture with halo-pollarding around selected winners so that the mixtures are preserved. This increases woodland resilience, tree growth rates and carbon storage in the pollarded trees and their roots (Chapter 2).

6. Defer decisions on which trees to retain in order to provide time to determine their growth rates, how they fit into the environment and how they respond to climate change.

7. Introduce national control policies on grey squirrels and deer (Chapter 6).

FIGURE 8.

Mixed deciduous and conifer plantation.

Conclusion

There are many claims to international emergencies in the biosphere, including loss of biodiversity, ecosystem collapse, loss of forest cover, plastic pollution and climate change. They all have the same origin – too many people taking too much out of a small planet. All are important but CO_2 pollution will be the most devastating if not resolved soon. Bill Gates has written an easy-to-read analysis of what needs doing titled 'How to Avoid a Climate Disaster: The Solutions We Have and the Breakthroughs We Need'.[12]

Sustainability is the key to our future. Afforestation has a small but important role in the big picture.[13,14]

Chapter 10

Properties and oddities

▼ Norbury Park Farm threshing barn.

▲ Gap pool spillway.

A manor, a moat and a World War II pillbox

Although we were mostly concerned with developing the woods and arable leys on the estate, there was also a pressing need to renovate some of the buildings. Many were poorly insulated and used fossil fuels for heating. As self-respecting carbon warriors, we wished to reduce our carbon footprints. To date, we have refurbished a few but others remain work-in-progress.

Map of Norbury Park buildings and monuments.

FIGURE 1.

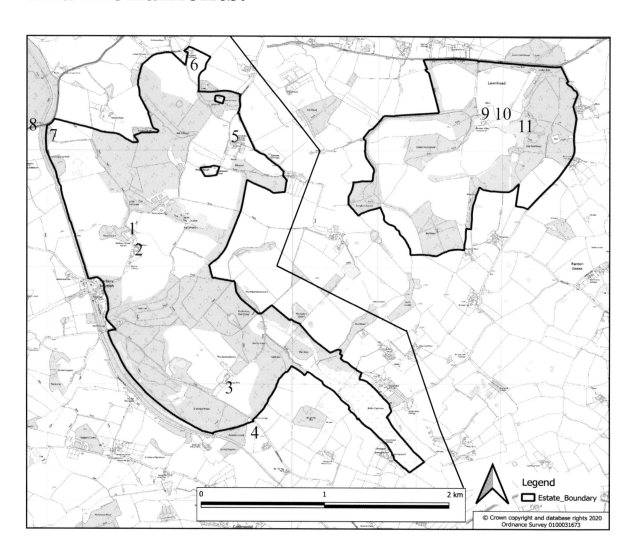

1.	Medieval moated site	5.	Knightley Grange cottage, stables and horse monument	9.	Ranton Abbey tower
2.	Norbury Manor farmhouse	6.	Knightley cottage buildings	10.	Ranton Abbey
3.	Norbury farmhouse and the 18th century threshing barn	7.	World War II pillbox	11.	Gap Pool
4.	Shelmore Lodge	8.	Shortest telegraph pole in the world		

In addition to the habitable buildings, there are other constructions and curiosities on or adjacent to the estate. To complete the story of Norbury Park, they are mentioned in this chapter (also see Chapter 1).

Medieval moated site

Built around the turn of the 12th century, a fine moated manor still existed in the 17th century (Chapter 1) but became neglected. Badly damaged by fire in the late 1700s, it was reduced to a ruin. Subsequently, most of the fine ashlar sandstone blocks were removed to construct Norbury Manor (see below) and renovate nearby Knightley church.

The central area became a cottage garden for many years, with a rim of large irregular stones. Trees, which had taken root in its low walls, gradually displaced the stones, which progressively tumbled into the weed-filled moat (Figure 2).

▼ **FIGURE 2.** *Moated site in 2012 before renovations.*

It was listed on the heritage at risk register for Historic England and was in a poor state.

In 2013, with a little financial input from us plus contributions from Natural England and English Heritage, the site was restored (Figure 3). Stones in the moat were replaced on the walls under the keen eyes of archaeologists, and the great-crested newts that were living there were rewarded with two specially built manors (piles of large stones) on the far bank. From a state of neglect the site was removed from the Historic England at risk register in 2014 and has regained its rightful place as one of the best medieval moats in Staffordshire.[1]

▲ **FIGURE 3.** *Moated site after renovations.*

▲ **FIGURE 4.** *Norbury Manor in 2021.*

Norbury Manor

Norbury Manor was built in the early 1800s as an estate farmhouse, using stones from the adjacent medieval manor (Figure 4). An adjoining set of farm buildings were constructed at the same time. It is a large and rather featureless manor built of unattractive dull brown Triassic sandstone. Until recently, it belonged to the Dale family (Chapter 1) but was brought under our ownership in 2020. It is currently being renovated with the use of modern insulation and will be warmed from an air source heat pump.

Norbury Park farmhouse and 18th-century threshing barn

▼ **FIGURE 5.**

Threshing barn and courtyard.

Norbury Park farm came into the hands of the Anson family in 1776. It was leased to various people until the 1980s when the farmhouse became the shooting lodge for Patrick Lichfield. He hosted many a good party, with royalty and friends enjoying his well-known pheasant shoot. Under our ownership, the house was renovated using modern insulation and is now heated from a woodchip boiler.

Behind the elegant frontage of the grade II listed house (Chapter 1) is a square courtyard built in the 1740s (Figure 5). One side is occupied by a fine oak-vaulted threshing barn, which for 20-odd years had been used as a rearing shed for pheasants, who produced a foot-deep layer of guano on the floor. While the brick walls were intact and the building stable, holes in the roof had allowed rain onto the original roof beams. In need of repairs and a little love, its damaged roof beams were replaced with oak beams from the estate (Figure 6). The building interior was refurbished as an office with meeting rooms. Now well insulated and with heat supplied from the woodchip boiler, the building is in keeping with modern housing standards.

▶ **FIGURE 6.**

260-year-old complex oak roof of the old barn.

Shelmore Lodge

A three-bedroomed lodge marks the southern edge of Norbury Park. Built early in the 19th century as a 'keeper's house' for Shelmore Wood, it was occupied until recently by Doris Bailey after she moved from Norbury Park farmhouse. She had been the main housekeeper and cook for Patrick Lichfield when he came shooting. We renovated it in 2015 (Figure 7 and Chapter 4, Figure 6).

▶ **FIGURE 7.**

Shelmore Lodge.

Knightley Grange cottage, stables and horse monument

Knightley Grange was a Victorian mansion that was cold and draughty, with high ceilings and a huge Mrs Beeton-style kitchen (Chapter 1, Figure 12). Built by Major Robert Hargreaves in the 1860s, it had been neglected for a long time. Needing an army of staff, it was too large for a modern family, too small for a school and too remote for offices. An attempt at renovation by Brian Dale came to nothing, leaving it in a poor state for 30 years. It was demolished in 2019 to expose Knightley Grange cottage to its rear with its associated Victorian stables (Figure 8). Alongside is a Victorian walled garden in good repair (Figure 9).

Sited on an escarpment near Hob Hill, the buildings afford long-distance views of the Shropshire hills – the Wrekin, the Clee Hills, the Long Mynd and the extinct volcanoes called the Brieddens on the border with Wales (Figure 10). Just beyond an ancient croquet lawn and behind a sandstone wall is a monument to a horse called Rock and several dogs (Figure 11). Owner Major Robert Hargreaves would ride his lands on his horse, and when Rock died he was buried with a view to die for (Figure 10).

◀ **FIGURE 8. (TOP)**
Knightley Grange cottage and stable block.

FIGURE 9. (MIDDLE)
Walled garden.

FIGURE 10. (BOTTOM)
View across young woodlands and Shropshire to the Briedden Hills in Wales.

FIGURE 11.
1883 monument to Rock.

Knightley Park Farm

At the north entrance to the estate is a row of old worksheds that are used as offices by arboriculturist and tree surgeon Rob Keyzor. An adjacent dilapidated Dutch barn was demolished and replaced with a showroom displaying Shelmore Timber products together with classrooms for training arborists. One large room houses a reconstructed oak tree, complete with gallery for training tree-climbers – the only one of its type in the UK (Figure 12).

▷ **FIGURE 12.**
Indoor oak tree for training arboriculturists.

> " One large room houses a reconstructed oak tree, complete with gallery for training tree-climbers – the only one of its type in the UK. "

World War II pillbox

Hidden in trees, a type 24 pillbox from World War II (Figure 13) guards High Bridge (Figure 14) on its eastern side. These field fortifications were constructed as part of a national defence programme in response to the threat of German invasion in 1940. This involved strengthening coastal fortifications and constructing protective lines stretching inland in order to slow down the progress of invading forces. Pillboxes were built throughout the country, particularly along strategic positions such as the deep canal cutting at Norbury. Needless to say, it was never used in battle.

The concrete structure is in poor condition with holes in its roof and sides. There is a far better example in nearby Market Drayton, also guarding a canal embankment.

▲ **FIGURE 13.** *Pillbox at Norbury park.*

High Bridge and the shortest telegraph pole in England

▼ FIGURE 14.
Short telegraph pole in High Bridge and a narrowboat.

Where the Shelmore canal embankment levels out at Norbury Junction, the Shropshire Union canal enters the mile-and-a-half long, 25-metre deep cutting of Grub Street. Crossing it is the rather curious 12.2-metre High Bridge, which carries the A519 Newcastle-under-Lyme to Newport road. It was built in 1832-33 by Thomas Telford but shortly after its construction, the pressure on the bridge from the cutting walls required the insertion of a strainer arch. On this was erected a cut-down telegraph pole, formerly used for communicating between towns along the canal. It is now no longer used, but stands up proudly to passing narrowboats (Figure 14).

Ranton Abbey tower

As mentioned in Chapter 1, the Augustinian Ranton Abbey was dissolved under Henry VIII in 1536. Little remains above ground other than the tower, a Romanesque archway and some ruins inside the adjacent Ranton Abbey, all thought to date from the 15th century. The large windows, perhaps originally containing stained glass, are now bricked up. Inside the 30-metre tower are several dilapidated wooden floors reached by a narrow spiral stone staircase. Fortunately, the roof and stone balustrade are intact, keeping the inside dry (Figure 15).

The tower would make great accommodation for a Landmark Trust holiday let property – but at what price?

◀ **FIGURE 15.**
Ranton Abbey tower.

Ranton Abbey

After the dissolution of the monasteries, Ranton Abbey was sold to the Harcourt family who converted part of the living quarters into an Elizabethan house. In the 1740s, this was converted to a Georgian house with some of the old abbey walls retained inside. There were numerous other rebuilding works after the 1790s when it was owned by the Lichfield family. However, it seems that throughout the centuries it has only been used intermittently – sometimes for shooting parties in the winter months and rented out on other occasions.

In World War II the house was requisitioned to billet the bodyguard of the exiled Queen Wilhelmina of The Netherlands (who herself was staying near London). In 1942, it burnt down and remains in a dilapidated state (Figure 16). Patrick Lichfield did renovate the stable block in the 1980s, converting it into an estate office with lodging (Figure 17).

▷ **FIGURE 16. (ABOVE)**
Ranton Abbey ruin.

▷ **FIGURE 17. (RIGHT)**
Ranton Abbey stable block.

Gap Pool and dam

The lake, created more than 100 years ago, was drained in World War II. By 1990, it resembled a young woodland. Under Patrick Lichfield's ownership, the trees were cleared, the lake dredged and the dam reconstructed to make a beautiful woodland setting (Figure 18). Nearby, he created a small arboretum among ancient oak trees.

Conclusion

It never ceases to amaze us that so much history can be found on a little-known estate in remote west Staffordshire. Yet there is Celtic, Roman, medieval and industrial history of considerable importance hidden within plain sight.

We have taken on the important and pleasurable activity of its preservation, maintenance and enhancement, both for the present and for future generations. However, there are no plans to renovate Ranton Abbey or Ranton Abbey tower. For the foreseeable future, they will remain as beautiful monuments to the past.

FIGURE 18.
View across Gap Pool.

FIGURE 19.
Building team. Lt to rt: Keith Stubbs, Andrea Evans and Joe Stubbs with his Ford Model T.

FIGURE 20.
Architect: Barry Joseph-Lester.

Chapter 11

What happens next?

▼ Halo-pollarding Scots pine with tree shears in a 30-year-old mixed species oak woodland.

A 17 inch diameter oak tree aged 140 years.

A 13 inch diameter larch tree aged 11 years.

Ideas are cheap. Putting them into practice is expensive.

The preceding chapters have described what we have undertaken at Norbury Park to sequester carbon and how we have achieved it. Needless to say, there is always more that can be done, more carbon that can be offset or sequestered. Our future plans maintain a focus on more CO_2 sequestration but we must also reduce our use of fossil fuels.

It is a very challenging target for the UK to become carbon neutral by 2050. Locking up carbon in trees and soil is only a small part of the equation, individuals must reduce their CO_2 footprint as well.

So first, what more can we achieve in terms of sequestration? As far as soil carbon storage on the arable land is concerned, we are fully committed to herbal leys and mob grazing with cattle over the next five years. Hopefully, this will increase soil organic matter by 1%, thereby maintaining carbon sequestration by approximately 3,000 tonnes per year. This will be a watch and wait policy as we have, as yet, minimal data on which to base any change of strategy.

As regards the woodlands, our thoughts are split between how we might manage the older ones

compared with the younger ones. By older, I mean those that are more than 30 years of age. Many contain oak trees but there are also beech woods (Figure 1) and mixed conifer plantations. If we follow our current thoughts, we will halo-thin single species mixtures and halo-pollard mixed species stands in order to maintain diversity (see Chapter 2). All will be targeted for good growth rates and fine timber.

The woodlands that contain oak trees around 150 years old will be nurtured perhaps for another 100 years, we hope, but how this might happen is undecided. Good timber remains our priority, so if they start to deteriorate, they will be felled and young trees put in their place. The best few will remain to be grand old souls.

The young woodlands remain work-in-progress. Their ages vary from 12 months to 12 years old and many will be part of ongoing observations and experiments. We want to see which mixtures grow faster, what combinations of two or more trees seem to be particularly resistant to infections and which non-native trees are hardy to frosts and drought.

Then there is the big question about thinning the young mixtures. We wish to select 'winners' at the

FIGURE 1.

Campions beech wood at Norbury Park.

earliest stage of canopy closure and protect their future. It will be interesting to compare growth rates in areas that are halo-pollarded with comparable areas that are halo-thinned to obtain firm scientific evidence on the benefits of the different regimens. Pollarding the taller trees is difficult manually so we are experimenting with tree shears that should be faster and safer (Figure 2).

More trees will be measured using dendrometers (tree-trunk girdling measurement tapes – Figure 3) to allow precise growth rates to be assessed. More accurate data on tree volumes and canopy size could be obtained using LIDAR assessments (laser imaging, detection and ranging), perhaps in collaboration with BIFoR.

Squirrel control remains a bugbear. It takes a lot of time and costs us £16,000 per year. We need more efficient and cheaper alternatives to Kania traps. Perhaps pine martens will eventually spread across from Wales, or squirrel contraceptive techniques will be developed. At present, these hoped-for developments are only distant possibilities.

▷ **FIGURE 2. (ABOVE)**
Halo-pollarding eight-year-old trees with shears.

▷ **FIGURE 3. (RIGHT)**
Dendrometer on a mature oak tree.

Nature and nurture always go hand-in-hand. There is much discussion about tree breeding for enhanced characteristics such as growth rates and form, but danger lurks. Introducing beneficial features into species might breed out disease resistance to some as yet untested pathogen. If crop breeding is taken as an example, then wide-ranging features such as disease resistance need to be included. Also, it will be important to grow young seedlings in higher CO_2 environments to check their suitability for future forests. But currently such experiments are beyond our focus.

Other wooded features of Norbury Estate need to be tackled. There are over 30 ponds (Figure 4), many created by clay removal for

▼ **FIGURE 4.**
Old marl pond.

brick-making (200 years ago there was a brick-kiln near Mill Haft). Most are surrounded by mature oak trees that need thinning to restore sunlight and life to the water.

Hedgerow trees need planting. Our 18 kilometres of borders and rough hedges can be enhanced by hedge-laying (Figure 5) and tree additions – perhaps exotic varieties to add beauty to the paths, rides and roads.

Beyond this, we must continue to focus on reducing our CO_2 emissions. The estate is currently over 5,000 tonnes carbon negative per year. With some adjustments to our current plans, could it be 6,000 tonnes? Adding solar panels or heat pumps to more buildings together with better insulation would help. We also need to process our waste wood more effectively. Sawdust from the mill and fire log waste is currently burnt but we plan to have it composted and returned to the land. More use will also be made of the mill offcuts for cladding and other long-term storage of wood products.

As regards future growth rates of the young woodlands, we have to be patient. Growing trees is a slow process. When we started, we wondered if we would ever see the saplings reach 12 metres. Now that they have, we want to see them reach 25 metres. In that time, we should have many results from the FACE experiment at BIFoR.

FIGURE 5.
Recently laid hedge.

Will the enhanced growth rates we are currently seeing persist in the high CO_2 environment or will they decline? Will the addition of nitrogen-fixing trees spur growth rates in oak trees and what will happen to trees that are watered and fed optimally?

With woodlands, patience is a virtue and a long life is a blessing.

"And into the forest I go, to lose my mind and find my soul"
John Muir

Appendices

Appendix 1. A typical example of an individual's annual production of CO_2 in the UK

Item/activity	CO_2 production
New medium-sized car (over a 10-yr lifetime)	17 tons
Recreation	1.95 tons
Heating	1.49 tons
Food production and consumption	1.39 tons
Home appliances, furnishing and construction	1.37 tons
Hygiene	1.34 tons
Clothing	1 ton
Commuting	0.81 tons
Air travel	0.68 tons
Education	0.49 tons
Television	0.215 tons
Tumbler dryer	0.059 tons
Electric oven	0.091 tons
Kettle	0.073 tons
Gas hob	0.071 tons
Standard light bulb	0.063 tons
Microwave	0.039 tons
	Total: 12.9 tons

Appendix 2. Largest 50 landowners in the UK (Google)

	Landowner	Hectares		Landowner	Hectares
1	Forestry Commission	890,328	27	Zambrano family	10,255
2	Ministry of Defence	445,913	28	Count Luca Rinaldo Contardo Padulli di Vighignolo	10,117
3	Crown Estate	274,553	29	Andrew Russell, 15th Duke of Bedford	8,690
4	National Trust and National Trust for Scotland	238,668	30	Stefan Persson	8,650
5	Royal Society for the Protection of Birds	134,359	31	Harworth Group	8,499
6	Richard Scott, Duke of Buccleuch and Queensberry	113,314	32	Edward Guinness, 4th Earl of Iveagh	8,363
7	Anders Holch Povlsen	88,371	33	HeidelbergCement	8,310
8	Duke of Atholl's Trusts	58,681	34	Corland Minerals	8,244
9	United Utilities	56,707	35	Queen Elizabeth II	8,094
10	Hugh Grosvenor, 7th Duke of Westminster	56,657	36	John Savile, 8th Earl of Mexborough	8,094
11	Duchy of Cornwall	54,634	37	Homes England	7,830
12	Department for Food and Rural Affairs (DEFRA)	47,070	38	John Clark	7,333
13	Church of England	42,493	39	Michael Stone	7,285
14	Dwr Cymru Cyfyngedig (Welsh Water)	31,556	40	Sir Richard John Tollemarche, 8th Baronet	7,247
15	John Whittaker (Peel Group)	28,329	41	Rathbone Brothers	7,225
16	Saltaire Water	28,329	42	Osprey Consortium	7,125
17	Cheung Kong Infrastructure Holdings	28,043	43	Valero Energy	6,967
18	MRH Minerals	27,493	44	Michael Cannon	6,476
19	Sheikh Mohammed Bin Rashid Al-Maktoum	25,496	45	Richard Kelvin-Hughes	6,475
20	Henry Somerset, 12th Duke of Beaufort	21,044	46	Kemble Water Holdings	6,470
21	Severn Trent	20,910	47	Pennon Group	6,401
22	LafargeHolcim	19,651	48	Merton College, University of Oxford	5,952
23	Robert Warren Miller	14,569	49	Taylor Wimpey	5,943
24	Hugh Lowther, 8th Earl of Lonsdale	14,273	50	Honourable Artillery Company	5,750
25	Sir James Dyson	13,355			Total: 2,966,913 ha
26	Roger Tempest	10,326			

Total UK land area is 24,250,000 hectares (94,530 square miles).

Appendix 3. Area of UK National Parks and their woodlands

Park	Location	Total area (ha)	Woodland area (ha)
Cairngorms	Scotland	452,800	18,391 (4%)
Lake District	England	236,200	28,500 (12%)
Yorkshire Dales	England	217,900	5,400 (2.5%)
Snowdonia	Wales	217,100	36,400 (17%)
Loch Lomond and the Trossachs	Scotland	186,500	52,300 (30%)
South Downs	England	162,700	10,000 (23%)
Peak District	England	143,700	420 (0.3%)
North York Moors	England	143,600	30,000 (23%)
Brecon Beacons	Wales	134,400	9,500 (7%)
Northumberland	England	104,900	21,000 (20%)
Dartmoor	England	95,400	11,300 (12%)
Exmoor	England	69,200	2500 (4%)
Pembrokeshire Coast	England	61,500	250 (0.4%)
New Forest	England	35,200	14,600 (41%)
Broads	England	30,200	2,371 (8%)
Total:		**1,733,551**	**242,871 (14%)**

Total wooded area of the UK is 13% (3,210,000 hectares).

Appendix 4. List of planted tree species at Norbury Park

(mostly bought from David Gwillam at Prees Heath Nurseries)

Common name	Scientific name
Alder	*Alnus glutinosa*
Alder, grey	*Alnus incana*
Alder, red	*Alnus rubra*
Ash	*Fraxinus excelsior*
Aspen	*Populus tremula*
Atlas cedar	*Cedrus atlantica*
Bald cypress	*Taxodium distichum*
Bay tree	*Laurus nobilis*
Bay willow	*Salix pentandra*
Beech	*Fagus sylvatica*
Beech, Antarctic	*Nothofagus antarctica*
Birch, black	*Betula nigra*
Birch, downy	*Betula pubescens*
Birch, silver	*Betula pendula*
Bird cherry	*Prunus padus*
Black locust	*Robinia pseudoacacia*
Black mulberry	*Morus nigra*
Black poplar	*Populus nigra*
Blackthorn	*Prunus spinosa*
Cedar of Lebanon	*Cedrus libani*
Common dogwood	*Cornus sanguinea*
Common privet	*Ligustrum vulgare*
Copper beech	*Fagus sylvatica 'purpurea'*
Crab apple	*Malus sylvestris*
Crack willow	*Salix fragilis*
Elm	*Ulmus*
Elm – disease resistant	*Columella, sapporo, autumn gold*
European larch	*Larix decidua*
Eucalyptus	*Eucalyptus regnans*
Eucalyptus	*Eucalyptus glaucenscens*
Eucalyptus	*Eucalyptus nitens*
Eucalyptus	*Eucalyptus gunneii*
Goat willow	*Salix caprea*

Common name	Scientific name
Fir, Douglas	*Pseudotsuga menziesii*
Guelder rose	*Viburnum opulus*
Handkerchief tree	*Davidia involucrata*
Hawthorn	*Crataegus monogyna*
Hazel	*Corylus avellana*
Himalayan cedar	*Cedrus deodara*
Holly	*Ilex aquifolium*
Hornbeam	*Carpinus betulus*
Hybrid larch	*Larix x eurolepis*
Indian bean tree	*Catalpa bignonioides*
Italian cypress	*Cupressus sempervirens*
Japanese red cedar	*Cryptomeria japonica*
Judas tree	*Cercis siliquastrum*
Juniper	*Juniperus communis*
Katsura	*Cercidiphyllum japonica*
Laburnum	*Laburnum anagyroides*
Lime, large leaf	*Tilia platyphyllos*
Lime, small leaf	*Tilia cordata*
Magnolia	*Grandiflora*
Magnolia	*campbelli Charles Raffill*
Magnolia	*sargentiana*
Magnolia, wild	*Sieboldii*
Maidenhair tree	*Ginkgo biloba*
Maple, field	*Acer campestre*
Maple, Japanese	*Acer palmatum 'Blood-good'*
Maple, Norway (variegated)	*Acer platanoides (A. platanoides 'Drummondii')*
Maple, silver	Acer saccharinum
Medlar	Mespilus germanica
Medlar tree 'Nottingham'	Mespilus germanica 'Nottingham'
Monkey puzzle tree	Araucaria araucana
Mulberry, white	Morus alba

Common name	Scientific name
Nootka cypress	Chamaecyparis nootkatensis
Oak, Algerian	Quercus canariensis
Oak, downy	Quercus pubescens
Oak, holm	Quercus ilex
Oak, pedunculate	Quercus robur
Oak, red	Quercus rubra
Oak, sessile	Quercus petraea
Oleaster	Elaeagnus umbellata
Pine, Bhutan	Pinus wallichiana
Pine, Corsican	Pinus nigra
Pine, Macedonian	Pinus peuce
Pine, maritime	Pinus pinaster
Pine, ponderosa	Pinus ponderosa
Pine, Scots	Pinus sylvestris
Plane	Platinus x hispanica
Redwood, coast	Sequoia sempervirens
Redwood, dawn	Metasequoia glyptostroboides
Roble	Nothofagus obliqua
Rowan	Sorbus aucuparia
Spindle	Euonymus europaeus
Spruce, blue	Picea pungens glauca
Spruce, Norway	Picea abies

Common name	Scientific name
Spruce, oriental	Picea orientalis
Spruce, Serbian	Picea omorika
Spruce, Sitka	Picea sitchensis
Spruce, weeping	Picea breweriana
Sweet chestnut	Castanea sativa
Sycamore	Acer psuedoplatanus
Tulip tree	Liriodendron tulipifera
Walnut, black	Juglans nigra
Walnut, common	Juglans regia
Walnut, white	Juglans cinerea
Wellingtonia (giant sequoia)	Sequoiadendron giganteum
Western catalpa	Catalpa speciosa
Western hemlock	Tsuga heterophylla
Western red cedar	Thuja plicata
White willow	Salix alba
Whitebeam	Sorbus aria
Whitebeam, Swedish	Sorbus intermedia
Wild cherry	Prunus avium
Wild pear	Pyrus communis
Wild service tree	Sorbus torminalis
Wych elm	Ulmus glabra
Yew	Taxus baccata

Appendix 5. Species in mixed conifer plantation

Common name	Scientific name
Austrian pine	*Pinus nigra austriaca*
Blue spruce	*Picea pungens glauca*
Coast redwood	*Sequoia sempervirens*
Corsican pine	*Pinus nigra corsicana*
Douglas fir	*Pseudotsuga taxifolia*
European larch	*Larix decidua*
Fraser fir	*Abies fraseri*
Grand fir	*Abies grandis*
Lawson cypress	*Chamaecyparis lawsoniana*
Lodgepole pine	*Pinus contorta*

Common name	Scientific name
Monterey pine	*Pinus radiata*
Noble fir	*Abies nobilis*
Norman fir	*Abies nordmanniana*
Norway spruce	*Picea abies*
Sitka spruce	*Picea sitchensis*
Scots pine	*Pinus sylvestris*
Serbian spruce	*Picea omorika*
Western hemlock	*Tsuga heterophylla*
Western red cedar	*Thuja plicata*
Yew	*Taxus baccata*

Appendix 6. Trees in watered plantations

Oak-dominated mixture

Common name	Scientific name
Common alder	*Alnus glutinosa*
Common hornbeam	*Carpinus betulus*
Fraser fir	*Abies fraseri*
Norway spruce	*Picea abies*
Pedunculate oak	*Quercus robur* (French)
Pedunculate oak	*Quercus robur* (English)
Pedunculate oak	*Quercus robur* (Dutch)
Scots pine	*Pinus sylvestris*
Silver birch	*Betula pendula*
Sycamore	*Acer pseudoplatanus*
Western red cedar	*Thuja plicata*

North-west Pacific mixture

Common name	Scientific name
Coast redwood	*Sequoia sempervirens*
Douglas fir	*Pseudotsuga menziesii*
Grand fir	*Abies grandis*
Red alder	*Alnus rubra*
Silver fir	*Abies alba*
Sitka spruce	*Picea sitchensis*
Western hemlock	*Tsuga heterophylla*
Western red cedar	*Thuja plicata*

Appendix 7. Tree species in the nitrogen-fixing experiment

Broadleaves	Oak	Conifers	Nitrogen-fixing trees
Silver birch	Pedunculate oak (French)	Douglas fir	Common alder
European sycamore	Pedunculate oak (English)	Western red cedar	Grey alder
Hornbeam		Coast redwood	Autumn elaeagnus
Sweet chestnut		Norway spruce	Common laburnum
Common beech		Scots pine	False acacia
Wild cherry		European yew	
Lime		Sitka spruce	
Tulip tree		Black pine	
Common walnut		Serbian spruce	
Eastern black walnut		European larch	
Field maple		Macedonian pine	
Common hawthorn		Lodgepole pine	
Wych elm			
Downy birch			
Sugar maple			
Rowan			
Wild service tree			

Appendix 8. Awards

Royal Forestry Society Sylva Trophy 2018

From RFS News, 19 July 2018:

In 2011 a new challenge prize was introduced by the RFS, the Sylva Trophy, donated by Patrick Evelyn, a direct descendent of John Evelyn, author of the seminal 17th century 'Sylva or a Discourse of Forest-trees and the propagation of Timber'. This trophy is presented annually to recognise a person or organisation who in the opinion of the RFS has made an outstanding contribution to forestry in its broadest sense.

Trotter L. Prof. Jo Bradwell awarded RFS Sylva Trophy. *Quarterly Journal of Forestry*. 2018; 18(112,4):220.

Jo Bradwell awarded RFS Sylva Trophy

Professor Jo Bradwell, who is credited with transforming the research landscape for forestry in England in less than a decade, has been awarded the Sylva Trophy.

The 2018 award recognises Professor Bradwell's 'can-do' attitude which has enabled ambitious research (long consigned to the 'too difficult' box) to be carried out.

With a £15M gift to the University of Birmingham, one of the largest philanthropic gifts to a UK university, Professor Bradwell and his wife, Dr Barbara Scott, inaugurated the Birmingham Institute of Forest Research (BIFoR). One of BIFoR's ground breaking projects is the Free-Air Carbon Enrichment (FACE) facility in old-growth oak woodland on Professor Bradwell's Norbury Park estate in Staffordshire.

Giving the citation at the RFS Excellence in Forestry Awards, Simon Lloyd, RFS Chief Executive, said: "This is a monumental undertaking; it stands comparison with the very largest scientific endeavours and is, in its way, the ecology equivalent of the Large Hadron Collider in Geneva. Carbon dioxide (CO_2) is added to the air in an oak woodland to measure the ecological response to the atmospheric composition expected by 2050. In every other way the woodland is left undisturbed as the experimental modification runs on – for a decade."

It is a project involving 20 research groups from across the world. Already, 150 events have brought the pressing issues of climate change and forest resilience to the attention of public, professionals, and education at all levels from primary to university.

The inauguration of BIFoR has also made possible the £1M Leverhulme Trust Doctoral Scholarship Programme called Forest Edge, which is the UK's biggest single injection of doctoral research into forest research. In addition, Professor Bradwell has brought the existing forest stands at Norbury Park into management and added over 300 acres of forest planting with new and unusual species mixes. The estate's commitment to sustainable best practice provides a national exemplar reaching right through the supply chain from new planting to biomass-fuelled combined heat and power and the highly-praised refurbishment of the estate's 18th-century threshing barn with estate-sourced timber.

▲ *Professor Jo Bradwell, recipient of the Sylva Trophy 2018. Credit: RFS/Brian Martin.*

Peter Savill Award

Woodland Heritage Peter Savill Award 2018. Woodland Heritage 18 July 2018.

Woodland Heritage is delighted to announce that the winner of this year's Peter Savill Award is Professor Jo Bradwell, an immunologist by profession, but whose support for innovation in science and research for the benefit of trees and forestry over the last five years has no parallel in the UK.

Professor Jo Bradwell studied medicine at the University of Birmingham and graduated in 1968, subsequently becoming a lecturer in the Department of Medicine then senior lecturer and professor in the Department of Immunology. He founded the Binding Site, a University spin-out company in 1983, which first developed diagnostic products for immune-deficiency and autoimmunity then a range of important novel cancer tests. The company has continued to grow and expand for 30 years and has won

The Peter Savill Award
For a significant contribution to British Forestry

THE PRIZE

Each year Woodland Heritage awards a prize to recognise the contribution of an individual who has significantly benefited British Forestry.

CRITERIA

The contribution to forestry made by the selected individual must be in sympathy with the objectives of Wood Heritage, and in one of the following areas of forestry: silviculture; research; wood processing; marketing; education.

Normally the prize will focus on a contribution to one of the above with an emphasise on Britain, broadleaves and lowland forestry, although not exclusively so.

the Queen's Award for Enterprise: International Trade three times, and the Queen's Award for Enterprise: Innovation once.

Thanks to a transformational gift of £15 million in 2013 from Prof. Bradwell, a new Institute for Forest Research (www.birmingham.ac.uk/research/activity/bifor/index.aspx) has been established by the University of Birmingham to study the impact of climate and environmental change on woodlands, and the resilience of trees to pests and diseases.

The gift of 15 million, which was donated by Professor Jo Bradwell and his wife Dr Barbara Scott, is one of the largest gifts to a UK university, and has enabled the University of Birmingham to establish a unique world leading centre and to be bold and ambitious in its research

intentions to understand how forests react to the combined threats of climate change and invasive pests and diseases.

In addition to on-campus laboratories, the Institute has created 'FACE: the Free Atmosphere Carbon Enrichment' facility, in Staffordshire, enabling scientists to take measurements from deep within the soil to above the tree canopy.

Autonomous sensors and instrumented trees allow scientists to take measurements continuously and remotely, over timescales ranging from seconds to decades.

Forests are critical components of global carbon, nutrient and water cycles, influencing the thermal balance of the planet directly and indirectly, and are home to more than half of all known species.

Forests deliver direct economic, environmental and social benefits, ranging from fuel and building materials, to the sense of well-being associated with a walk in the woods. More subtly, forests also deliver services that underpin the production of food, clean water, and the breakdown of waste production. As human populations have expanded, increasing pressures have been placed on forests, with the 20th century witnessing the steepest rise in rates of deforestation.

The dynamic responses of forest to combinations of climate change and pests and diseases are only partially understood, because there have been too few experiments on established unmanaged (wild) forests of sufficient scientific depth and duration.

As Professor Jo Bradwell explained: "The UK has the lowest woodland cover of any large European country because of deforestation over the centuries. What little we have remaining is now under serious threat from climate change and imported tree diseases. The new forestry institute will increase our understanding of these challenges in order to help planners, owners and foresters maintain and improve the health of our woods."

Lewis Scott, co-founder of Woodland Heritage, said: "We are delighted to announce that Professor Jo Bradwell is to be the recipient of the Peter Savill Award 2018, in recognition of the unique contribution that he had made to the world of forestry both in the UK and internationally, and in such a short period of time. Members of Woodland Heritage will have the chance to witness not just the amazing facilities at 'FACE' at this year's Field Weekend, but also the working, woodland estate at Norbury Park, including how over one hundred different species are faring in a unique test of which trees might be most suitable to grow in the UK in the future."

Appendix 9. Sovereign grass mix from Cotswold Seeds

	kg per acre	
1	3.00	AberWolf intermediate diploid perennial ryegrass (new variety) 21.43%
2	1.00	Glenariff intermediate diploid perennial ryegrass 7.14%
3	3.50	Dunluce intermediate tetraploid perennial ryegrass 25.00%
4	2.50	Seagow intermediate tetraploid perennial ryegrass (new variety) 17.86%
5	2.00	AberAvon late diploid perennial ryegrass 14.28%
6	1.00	Presto Timothy 7.14%
7	0.25	AberPearl small leaf white clover 1.67%
8	0.50	Crusader medium leaf white clover 3.57%
9	0.25	Barblanca large leaf white clover 1.78%
Total: 14 kg per acre		

Appendix 10. Herbal leys mix from Cotswold Seeds

	Weight (%)	Species/cultivar	Benefits
1	1.60 kg (1.6)	Hybrid ryegrass (AberEcho)	Biomass
2	1.50	Cocksfoot: early-growing light land grass	Biomass and deep-rooted
3	0.85 kg (0.85)	Perennial ryegrass: persistent grazing grass	Biomass
4	0.60 kg (0.6)	Promesse Timothy: long-term species, late-growing	Biomass, deep-rooted
5	0.50 kg (0.5)	Laura meadow fescue: adaptable grass growing well on less fertile soils	Biomass
6	0.40 kg (0.4)	Quantum tall fescue	Biomass, deep-rooted
7	0.40 kg (0.4)	AstonEnergy tetraploid: perennial ryegrass	Biomass
8	0.20	Aran white clover: high-protein, long-term legume	Biomass, nitrogenator
9	0.30 kg (0.3)	AberHerald white clover: high-protein, long-term legume	Nitrogenator
10	0.50 kg (0.5)	Dawn alsike clover: medium-term legume suited to heavier soils	Nitrogenator, deep-rooted
11	0.20 kg (0.2)	Leo birdsfoot trefoil: tanniferous legume lasting 3-4 years	Nitrogenator, worming
12	1.75 kg (1.75)	Sainfoin: tanniferous legume	Worming, drought tolerant, nitrogenator
13	1.00 kg (1)	Sweet clover: short-term legume	Deep-rooted, drought tolerant, nitrogenator, biomass
14	0.40 kg (0.4)	Chicory: mineral-rich, forage herb	Very deep-rooted, worming properties, nutrients: Co
15	0.20 kg (0.2)	Plantain: forage herb	Deep rooted, nutrients: Cu, I, Se, Zn
16	0.75 kg (0.75)	Burnet: herb	Deep-rooted, drought tolerant, nutrients: Co.
17	0.10 kg (0.1)	Yarrow: persistent forage herb	Deep-rooted, drought tolerant, nutrients: Mn, Cu, I
18	2.00 kg (2)	Early English vetch	Nitrogenator, biomass
19	0.50 kg (0.5)	Lucerne, pre-inoculated: perennial legume	Drought tolerant, nitrogenator
20	0.20 kg (0.2)	Crested dogstail: small grass	Biomass, deep-rooted
21	0.20 kg (0.2)	Smooth-stalked meadow grass	Biomass, deep-rooted
22	0.25 kg (0.25)	Virgo Pajbjerg yellow trefoil: early growth	Nitrogenator
23	0.60 kg (0.6)	Red clover	Nitrogenator, deep-rooted and biomass
	Total: 16.00 kg per acre		

Nutrients: Cu: copper; Co: cobalt; I: iodine; Mn: manganese; Se: selenium; Zn: zinc.

Appendix 11. A few of the ongoing studies at BIFoR FACE

Below-ground vegetation, litter and soil processes	Oak	Atmospheric processes	Water (FACE arrays)
Fine root development	Camera traps are installed through the woodland to monitor mammal activity	Wind speed	Soil moisture (gravimetric and volumetric)
Soil CO_2, H_2O fluxes		CO_2, H_2O, CH_4 fluxes	Throughfall precipitation (ground level)
N mineralization and N_2O source partitioning studies.		Solar and net radiation	Groundwater levels and soil surface temperature
Soil sampling and lab analysis		Air temperature and relative humidity profile	Field precipitation (ground level)
pH, soil type, organic matter content, bulk density			
Leaf litter			

Above-ground vegetation

- Green chromatic coordinate (GCC) and red chromatic coordinate (RCC)
- Phenology and biodiversity observations, including bryophyte and deadwood surveys
- Tree stem growth – LIDAR surveys (includes tree height), dendrometers (manual and automated)
- Tissue samples of green leaves taken from the top/middle/bottom of canopy for oak trees and also tissue samples from the other three key species of tree (hazel, hawthorn and sycamore) biobanked for chemical analysis
- Tissue samples of buds and catkins biobanked for future research
- Leaf area measurements of green leaves sampled from top/middle/bottom of canopy for the four key species of tree (oak, hazel, hawthorn and sycamore)
- Leaf area index – both hemispherical and direct methods

Glossary

Acre	An area of 4,840 square yards: nearly 70 yards square. 2.5 acres equals one hectare
Afforestation	Establishment of a forest in an area where there was no previous tree cover
Agricultural land	Land used for crops and animal rearing
Air-source heat-pump	A reverse refrigerator that pumps heat from air or soil into buildings
Alluvial	Alluvial soils are soils deposited by surface water
Anthelmintic	A compound that acts on parasitic worms (helminths)
Arable land	Land used for crops
Arable land grading	A measure of the quality of land, from 1 to 5, with 1 the best and 5 the worst
Arborist	Tree surgeon
Archaea	A large group of primitive, bacteria-like organisms
Ashlar	Masonry made of large square-cut stones, used as a facing on walls of brick or stone rubble
Beat-up	Replacing young dead trees in a woodland. Typically, 5% in the first year
Carbon balance	The difference between the amount of carbon emitted and the amount captured/sequestered
Canopy closure	The stage at which the canopies of individual trees meet in a young plantation
Carbon neutral	When carbon emissions and sequestration are equal
Carbon offset	Reduction in emissions of carbon dioxide or other greenhouse gases made in order to compensate for emissions made elsewhere
Carbon sequestration/ capture	A natural or artificial process by which carbon dioxide is removed from the atmosphere and held in solid or liquid form
CO_2	Carbon dioxide

CO_2e	Carbon dioxide equivalent. Eg. 1.0 megawatt (mW) of solar power is 0.37 tonnes of CO_2e ie. one tonne of CO_2 is equivalent to 2.7 megawatts (mW) of solar power (variable sources)
Composting	Process of storing plant material for decomposing and then adding to soil
Coppicing	Cutting trees to their stumps to encourage shoot regeneration
Cultivar	A plant that has been cultivated for desirable characteristics
Dbh	Tree diameter at breast height (a standard tree measurement at 1.4 m)
Deciduous	Shedding leaves at the end of the growing season
Dreys	Squirrel nests for sleeping, breeding and winter warmth
Epicormic growth	Suppressed buds on a tree trunk that grow when exposed to sunlight
Free growth	Trees with canopies in full sunlight to allow maximum growth rates
Fungal hyphae	Thread-like filaments from fungi
Halo-pollarding	Cutting back surrounding and competing trees to a height of two metres
Halo-thinning	Removing surrounding competing trees
Harrow	Cultivating tool set with spikes, teeth, or discs and used primarily for breaking up and smoothing the soil
Hectare/ha	An area of 100 m x 100 m.
Helminths	Parasitic worms, particularly of the gut, that cause a wide variety of infectious diseases
Herbal ley	Mixture of grasses, legumes and herbs planted on arable land
Humus	The organic component of soil, formed by the decomposition of leaves and other plant material by soil micro-organisms
kW	1,000 watts. A measure of electrical energy
kWh	1,000 watts of energy over an hour

Mob grazing	Rotating herds of cattle through a series of restricted areas of pasture
Monoculture	A forest area where all the trees are of the same type
Native woodlands	Contains trees that are found naturally in the UK
Nematodes	Worms of the huge phylum Nematoda, such as roundworms or threadworms – some of the most abundant animals on earth
Nitrogen fixation	Chemical conversion of atmospheric nitrogen into compounds by microbes that can then be used by plants. Associated with the roots of some plant species
Over-yielding	Unexpectedly high growth rates seen when mixtures of plants are grown together, also knowns as the "Darwin Effect"
Pathogen	A bacterium, virus, or other micro-organism that can cause disease
Photosynthesis	Light-powered conversion of carbon dioxide (CO_2) and water (H_2O) into glucose ($C_6H_{12}O_6$) and oxygen (O_2)
Phylogenetic	The evolutionary relationship between different species
Phylum	A major taxonomic division of living organisms
Pollarding	Removal of tree branches above two metres which promotes the growth of branches
Protozoa	A phylum or grouping of phyla which comprises single-celled, microscopic animals
Provenance	Place of origin
Random intimate mixture	Tree planting with numerous species mixed randomly together
Reforestation	Regeneration or replanting forest areas that have been destroyed or damaged
Rhizotron	An underground chamber with transparent walls used to study plant roots
Rides	Tracks or wide paths in woodlands to allow access
Rugosity (surface roughness)	Complexity and density of a forest canopy

Sequestration	The action of chemically sequestering or binding a substance such as carbon dioxide
Silviculture	Care and cultivation of woodlands
Silage	Grass or other green fodder compacted and stored in airtight conditions for winter feed
Solar PV	Photovoltaic panels that convert the sun's energy into electricity
Standard deviation	A measure of distribution of a data set. If a set of data is normally distributed about its mean, then about two-thirds of the data points will lie within one standard deviation of the mean value, and about 95% of the data points will lie within two standard deviations of the mean value
Symbiosis	Mutually beneficial interactions between different organisms
Tillage	Preparation of land for growing crops
Ton	A UK ton of 2,240 pounds or 1016.05 kg
Tonnes	A metric tonne of 1,000 kg
Tree-rack	Removal of a line of trees to allow access for management
Wood wide web	Complex underground webs of roots, fungi and bacteria that connect trees and plants to one another
Xylem	Tubes carrying water and minerals from roots to branches and leaves
Yield-class curves and tables	Productive capacity of a monoculture woodland in cubic meters of timber per hectare per year. They are based upon characteristic growth curves of a given species and a given management regimen.

Bibliography

Chapter 1. Norbury Park Estate – a brief history

1. Bax S. A National Mapping Programme Project Report. Staffordshire: Aerial Survey of Gnosall, Kidsgrove and Talke. Historic England Project Number 6613. Page 15. Archaeological Research Services Ltd.

2. Great Domesday 1086, Folio 248.

3. Noble M. Knightley. In: *Memoirs of the Protectoral-house of Cromwell.* Volume 2, p.91–8 & p.91. 1787. Birmingham: Pearson & Rollason

4. Burghers, M 1684 Table (illustration) 19. In: Plot, R 1686 *The Natural History of Staffordshire.* Oxford.

5. Medd J. Field Days: Patrick Lichfield. *The Rake Magazine.* 1970. Issue 45.

6. Dale Family. The Life of Brian James Dale. Caynham House, Ludlow, Shropshire. 1995

Chapter 2. Woods and carbon storage

1. Ranton Diamond Wood. The Royal Record of Tree Planting for the Diamond Jubilee of Queen Elizabeth 2012. The Woodland Trust. 2012. p6 & 84

2. Liang J, Crowther TW, Picard N, Wiser S, Zhou M, Alberti G *et al.* Positive biodiversity-productivity relationship predominant in global forests. *Science.* 2016;354(6309): 196.

3. Bradwell J, Argyle P, Shorthouse D, Daniels R. Increased growth rates in complex tree mixtures. *Quarterly Journal of Forestry.* 2019;113(1): 86–87.

4. Kerr G, Forster J. Can we grow oak to 60cm DBH in less than 100 years in Britain? *Quarterly Journal of Forestry.* 2018:112(3): 156–162.

5. Hamilton GJ, Christie JM. Forest Management Tables (Metric). Forestry Commission Booklet No. 34. 1971. London: HMSO.

6. Barne M. Growing Oak Faster. 2021. Woodland Heritage Annual Report.

7. Bladon F. 100 Years of forest research in Wessex – A study by the Wessex Silvicultural Group. *Quarterly Journal of Forestry.* 2020;114(4): 260–267.

8. Spencer J. Forest resilience in British forests, woods and plantations. *Quarterly Journal of Forestry.* 2019;113(2): 109–114.

9. Kerr G, Haufe J, Stokes V, Mason B. Establishing robust species mixtures. *Quarterly Journal of Forestry.* 2020;114(3): 162–168.

10. Reynolds C, Jinks R, Kerr G, Parratt M, Mason B. Providing the evidence base to diversify Britain's forest: initial results from a new generation of species trials. *Quarterly Journal of Forestry.* 2021;115(1): 26–37.

11. Whyatt H, Wight F, Bradwell J. Investigating nitrogen fixing trees in intimate species mixtures. In: Trees for the future – Diversity and complexity for resilience and carbon storage. *Association of Applied Biologists.* Conference, November 2021.

Chapter 3. How woodland tree mixtures increase carbon storage

1. Liang J, Crowther TW, Picard N, Wiser S, Zhou M, Alberti G *et al.* Positive biodiversity-productivity relationship predominant in global forests. *Science.* 2016;354(6309): 196.

2. Huang Y, Chen Y, Castro-Izaguirre N, Baruffol M, Brezzi M, Lang A *et al.* Impacts of species richness on productivity in a large-scale subtropical forest experiment. *Science.* 2018;362: 80–83.

3. Grossman JJ, Cavender-Bares J, Hobbie S, Reich PB, Montgomery RA. Species richness and traits predict overyielding in stem growth in an early-successional tree diversity experiment. *Ecology.* 2017; 98(10): 2601–2614.

4. Darwin C. *On The Origin of Species by Means of Natural Selection.* 6th Edn. Chapter IV, p. 88. 1859. New York: D Appleton & Co.

5. Gough CM, Atkins JW, Fahey RT. High rates of primary production in structurally complex forests. *Ecology.* 2019;100(10): e02864.

6. Williams LJ, Paquette A, Cavender-Bares J, Messier C, Reich PB. Spatial complementarity in tree crowns

explains overyielding in species mixtures. *Nature: Ecology and Evolution.* 2017;1(4): 63.

7. Pretzsch H. Growth and Structure in Mixed-Species Stands compared with Monocultures: Review and Perspectives. In: Bravo-Oviedo A, Pretzsch H, del Río M (Eds). *Dynamics, Silviculture and Management of Mixed Forests: Managing Forest Ecosystems.* p173. 2018. Springer International Publishing.

8. Fichtner A, Schnabel F, Bruelheide H, Kunz M, Mausolf K, Schuldt A *et al.* Neighbourhood diversity mitigates drought impacts on tree growth. *Journal of Ecology.* 2020;108(3): 865–875.

9. Rottstock T, Joshi J, Kummer V, Fischer M. Higher plant diversity promotes higher diversity of fungal pathogens, while it decreases pathogen infection per plant. *Ecology.* 2014;95(7): 1907–1917.

10. Keesing F, Ostfeld RS. Is biodiversity good for your health? The benefits of diversity. *Science.* 2015;349(6245): 235–236.

11. Civitello DJ, Cohen J, Fatima H, Halstead NT, Liriano J, McMahon TA et al. Biodiversity inhibits parasites: Broad evidence for the dilution effect. *Proceedings of the National Academy of Sciences of the USA.* 2015:112(28): 8667–8671.

12. Bauhus J et al. Ecological Stability of Mixed-Species Forests. In: Pretzsch H, Forrester DI and Bauhus (Eds). *Mixed-Species Forests; Ecology and Management.* p. 365. 2017. Berlin, Heidelberg: Springer-Verlag.

13. Evans I, Bromley R, Ashpole M, Ziari D, Pua A, Raw M and Luna E. Effect of mixed plantations and neighbouring species in the resistance to ash dieback disease. *Mixed species forests: Risks, Resilience and Management* 2020; abstract p33. Lund, Sweden.

14. Hendriks M, Mommer L, de Caluwe H, Smit-Tiekstra AE, van der Putten WH, de Kroon H. Independent variations of plant and soil mixtures reveal soil feedback effects on plant community overyielding. *Journal of Ecology.* 2013;101(2): 287–297.

15. Binkley D. Seven decades of stand development in mixed and pure stands of conifers and nitrogen-fixing red alder. *Canadian Journal of Forest Research.* 2003;33(11): 2274–2279.

16. 16. Forrester DI, Bauhus J, Khanna PK. Growth dynamics in a mixed-species plantation of Eucalyptus globulus and Acacia mearnsii. *Forest Ecology and Management.* 2004;193: 81–95.

17. Clark JR, Hemery GE, Savill PS. Early growth and form of common walnut (Juglans regia L.) in mixture with tree and shrub nurse species in southern England. *Forestry.* 2008;81(5): 631–644.

18. Perakis SS, Pett-Ridge JC. Nitrogen-fixing red alder trees tap rock-derived nutrients. *Proceedings of the National Academy of Sciences of the USA.* 2019;116(11): 5009–5014.

19. Cemorowoodcraft. Ring porous wood. 4 January 1991. https://cemorowoodcraft.blogspot.com/1991/01/ring-porous-wood.html

20. Büntgen U, Krusic PJ, Piermattei A, Coomes DA, Esper J, Myglan VS et al. Limited capacity of tree growth to mitigate the global greenhouse effect under predicted warming. *Nature Communications.* 2019;10: 2171.

Chapter 5. Farming a revolution – carbon storage on arable land.

1. Montgomery DR. *Growing a Revolution – Bringing our soil back to life.* 2017. WW Norton & Co.

2. Darwin C. *The Formation of Vegetable Mould, through the Action of Worms, with Observations on their Habits.* 1881. John Murray.

3. Cotswold Seeds Ltd, Cotswold Business Village, Moreton-in-Marsh, Gloucestershire GL56 0JQ

4. Darwin C. *On the Origin of Species by Means of Natural Selection,* 6th Edn. Chapter IV, p. 88. 1859. John Murray.

5. Hungate BA, Barbier EB, Ando AW, Marks SP, Reich PB, van Gestel N *et al.* The economic value of grassland species for carbon storage. *Science Advances.* 2017;3(4): e1601880.

6. Fornara DA, Tilman D. Plant functional composition

influences rates of soil carbon and nitrogen accumulation. *Journal of Ecology.* 2008; 96(2): 314–322. doi: 10.1111/j.1365-2745.2007.01345.x

Chapter 6. Pests and diseases.

1. O'Bryen, B. Squirrel control. *Quarterly Journal of Forestry.* 2021;115(1): 11.
2. Mayle, BA. Britain's woodlands under threat; grey squirrels and the risk they pose to European woodlands. *Trees, Journal of the International Tree Foundation.* 2005;65: 9–11.
3. Dutton JCF. *The Grey Squirrel Management Handbook.* 2016. Suffolk: European Squirrel Initiative.
4. European Squirrel Initiative. £40 million per annum timber loss from grey squirrels. Press release. https://www.europeansquirrelinitiative.org/wp-content/uploads/2019/05/40-MILLION-PER-ANNUM-TIMBER-LOSS-FROM-GREY-SQUIRRELS.pdf. [Accessed 30 April 2021].
5. Whyatt H, Wight F, Smith R, Malkin A, Shorthouse D, Bradwell J. Successful Grey Squirrel Control at Norbury Park Estate. *Quarterly Journal of Forestry.* 2021; 115(3): 183-188.
6. Mayle BA, Proudfoot J, Poole, J. Influence of tree size and dominance on incidence of bark stripping by grey squirrels to oak and impact on tree growth. *Forestry: An International Journal of Forest Research.* 2009; 82(4): 431–444 https://doi.org/10.1093/forestry/cpp015
7. 7. Red Squirrels United. Establishing efficacy of the Kania Trap. Presentation. 2018 http://www.redsquirrelsunited.org.uk/wp-content/uploads/2018/10/Kania-Trap-Presentation-WEB.pdf.
8. Royal Forestry Society. Squirrel Control Case Study – Plashett Wood. Available at: https://www.rfs.org.uk/news/grey-squirrels/. [Accessed 30 April 2021]
9. Royal Forestry Society. *Counting the Cost of Squirrel Control in an Oak Plantation.* 2020 https://www.rfs.org.uk/media/492973/counting-the-cost-of-squirrel-damage-in-oak-plantations.pdf
10. Royal Forestry Society. *Counting the Cost of Squirrel Damage in a Small Wood.* 2020 https://www.rfs.org.uk/media/809344/counting-the-cost-of-grey-squirrel-damage-in-a-small-wood.pdf.
11. Forest Research. Controlling grey squirrels in forests and woodlands in the UK. UK Forestry Standard Technical Note. Available at: https://www.forestresearch.gov.uk/research/controlling-grey-squirrels-forests-and-woodlands-uk/. [Accessed 30 April 2021].
12. Stocks JJ et al. Genomic basis of European ash tree resistance to ash dieback fungus. *Nature Ecology & Evolution* 2019; 3: 1686–1696.

Chapter 7. Birmingham Institute of Forest Research

1. Read DJ, Freer-Smith PH, Morison JIL, Hanley N, West CC, Snowdon P (Eds). Combating climate change – a role for UK forests. An assessment of the potential of the UK's trees and woodlands to mitigate and adapt to climate change. 2009. Edinburgh: the Stationery Office. Available at: https://www.forestresearch.gov.uk/documents/2062/SynthesisUKAssessmentfinal.pdf
2. Tollefson J. Experiment aims to steep rainforest in carbon dioxide. *Nature.* 2013;496: 405–406.
3. Hart KM, Curioni G, Blaen P, Harper NJ, et al. Characteristics of free air carbon dioxide enrichment of a northern temperate mature forest. *Glob Change Biol* 2019; 26(2): 1023–1037.
4. Gardner A, Ellsworth DS, Crous KY, Pritchard J, MacKenzie A. R. 2021. Is photosynthetic enhancement sustained through three years of elevated CO2 exposure in 175-year old Quercus robur?, *Tree Physiol.* In press.

Chapter 9. Politics, polices and people

1. Victor DG, Akimoto K, Kaya Y, Yamaguchi M, Cullenward D, Hepburn C. Prove Paris was more than paper promises. *Nature.* 2017;548 (7665): 25–27.
2. Rogelj J, den Elzen M, Höhne, N, Fransen T, Fekete H,

Winkler H *et al.* Paris Agreement climate proposals need a boost to keep warming well below 2°C. *Nature.* 2016;534 (7609): 631–639.

3. Boffey D. Court orders Royal Dutch Shell to cut carbon emissions by 45% by 2030. *The Guardian.* 26 May 2021.

4. United Nations. Kyoto Protocol to the United Nations Framework Convention on Climate Change. 1998. New York: United Nations. Available at: https://unfccc.int/resource/docs/convkp/kpeng.pdf

5. Department for Business, Energy & Industrial Strategy, Prime Minister's Office, 10 Downing Street, the Rt Hon Alok Sharma MP, and the Rt Hon Boris Johnson MP. UK sets ambitious new climate target ahead of UN Summit. Press release. 3 December 2020. www.gov.uk/government/news/uk-sets-ambitious-new-climate-target-ahead-of-un-summit

6. Department for Business, Energy and Industrial Strategy, Prime Minister's Office, 10 Downing Street, the Rt Hon Kwasi Kwarteng MP, the Rt Hon Alok Sharma MP, and the Rt Hon Boris Johnson MP. UK enshrines new target in law to slash emissions by 78% by 2035. Press release. 20 April 2021. https://www.gov.uk/government/news/uk-enshrines-new-target-in-law-to-slash-emissions-by-78-by-2035

7. Department for Environment, Food and Rural Affairs. The England Trees Action Plan 2021–2024. 2021. London: Department for Environment, Food and Rural Affairs. Available at: https://www.gov.uk/government/publications/england-trees-action-plan-2021-to-2024

8. Climate Change Committee. Net Zero – The UK's contribution to stopping global warming. 2019. Climate Change Committee. Available at: https://www.theccc.org.uk/publication/net-zero-the-uks-contribution-to-stopping-global-warming/

9. Manning F, Ffoulks C. The role of woodland and agroforestry to meet Net Zero. 23 April 2020. https://www.adas.uk/News/the-role-of-woodland-and-agroforestry-to-meet-net-zero

10. Di Sacco A, Hardwick KA, Blakesley D, Brancalion PHS, Breman E, Cecilio Rebola L et al. Ten golden rules for reforestation to optimize carbon sequestration, biodiversity recovery and livelihood benefits. Glob Chang Biol. 2021;27(7):1328–1348.

11. Mwai P. Did Ethiopia plant four billion trees this year? BBC News. 20 December 2019. https://www.bbc.co.uk/news/world-africa-50813726.

12. Gates B. *How to Avoid a Climate Disaster: The Solutions We Have and the Breakthroughs We Need.* 2021. New York: Alfred A Knopf.

13. Forestry Commission. Responding to the climate emergency with new trees and woodlands: A guide to help local authorities and landowning businesses achieve net zero. Bristol: Forestry Commission. 2020. Available at: https://www.gov.uk/government/publications/leaflet-responding-to-the-climate-emergency-with-new-trees-and-woodlands.

14. Read DJ, Freer-Smith PH, Morison JIL, Hanley N, West CC, Snowdon P (Eds). Combating climate change – a role for UK forests. An assessment of the potential of the UK's trees and woodlands to mitigate and adapt to climate change. 2009. Edinburgh: the Stationery Office. Available at: https://www.forestresearch.gov.uk/documents/2062/SynthesisUKAssessmentfinal.pdf

Chapter 10. Properties and oddities

1. Reid ML. Norbury Manor Medieval Site, Staffordshire. Scheduled Monument List Entry Number: 1011875. A report for the owner and estate managers of Norbury Park. 2014.

Index

Permissions

Chapter 1, figure 9. Reproduced courtesy of Staffordshire Record Office.

Chapter 1, figure 11. Reproduced courtesy of Staffordshire Record Office.

Chapter 3, figure 2. From Liang J, Crowther TW, Picard N, Wiser S, Zhou M, Alberti G et al. Positive biodiversity-productivity relationship predominant in global forests. Science. 2016;354(6309): 196. Reprinted with permission from AAAS.

Chapter 3, figure 3. From Huang Y, Chen Y, Castro-Izaguirre N, Baruffol M, Brezzi M, Lang A et al. Impacts of species richness on productivity in a large-scale subtropical forest experiment. Science. 2018;362: 80–83. Reprinted with permission from AAAS.

Chapter 3, figure 6. From Gough CM, Atkins JW, Fahey RT. High rates of primary production in structurally complex forests. Ecology. 2019;100(10): e02864. Reprinted with permission from AAAS.

Chapter 3, figure 12. From Keesing F & Ostfeld RS. Is biodiversity good for your health? The benefits of diversity. Science. 2015;349(6245): 235-236. Reprinted with permission from AAAS.

Chapter 5, figure 8. From Fornara DA and Tilman D. Plant functional composition influences rates of soil carbon and nitrogen accumulation. Journal of Ecology. 2008; 96(2): 314–322. doi: 10.1111/j.1365-2745.2007.01345.x. Reprinted with permission from John Wiley and Sons and Copyright Clearance Center.